Inspired by
Thomas Hardy

An Anthology of Students' Works

2020

*'Painting on wood' of Thomas Hardy by Pete Sheridan
(with permission from owner Faysal Mikdadi).*

Inspired by
Thomas Hardy

An Anthology of Students' Works

2020

Edited by Faysal Mikdadi

Roving
Press

Step-Up Books

© 2020 The Thomas Hardy Society
Published by Roving Press Ltd under the Step-Up Books imprint
4 Southover Cottages, Frampton, Dorset, DT2 9NQ, UK
Tel: +44 (0)1300 321531, www.rovingpress.co.uk

Distributed by The Thomas Hardy Society
c/o Dorset County Museum, Dorchester, Dorset DT1 1XA
Tel: +44 (0)1305 251501
E-mail: info@hardysociety.org
www.hardysociety.org

The cover ink drawing of Thomas Hardy is by Samima Parvin.

First published 2020 by Roving Press Ltd

ISBN: 978-1-906651-367

British Library Cataloguing in Publication Data
A catalogue record for this book is available from the British Library

Set in 11.5/13 pt Minion by Beamreach Printing (www.beamreachuk.co.uk)
Printed and bound in England by Beamreach Printing

Contents

Poems composed at Max Gate by Rose Day

Bryanston School

Dorchester Middle School

Dorset Studio School

Greenwood Academy

St Osmund's Church of England Middle School

Southlands School

---

[1] Teaching Assistant.
[2] Teacher of English.
[3] Head of English.
[4] Teaching Assistant.
[5] Staff

The Taunton Academy

The Thomas Hardye School

Individual Submissions from Other Schools

Afterword

Acknowledgements

The Schreckhorn
Thomas Hardy

(With thoughts of Leslie Stephen)
(June 1897)

Aloof, as if a thing of mood and whim;
Now that its spare and desolate figure gleams
Upon my nearing vision, less it seems
A looming Alp-height than a guise of him
Who scaled its horn with ventured life and limb,
Drawn on by vague imaginings, maybe,
Of semblance to his personality
In its quaint glooms, keen lights, and rugged trim.

At his last change, when Life's dull coils unwind,
Will he, in old love, hitherward escape,
Enter this silent adamantine shape,
And his low voicing haunt its slipping snows
When dawn that calls the climber dyes them rose?

The credit for all that is fair in this Anthology undoubtedly goes to the wonderful students who took part in the Thomas Hardy Creative Workshops from early January to mid-March 2020. The young poets were enthusiastic, responsive and very sensitive in their readings of some of Thomas Hardy's and several other poets' works. The editor was highly privileged and deeply honoured to have had this opportunity of sharing evocative and memorable poetry and some prose with so many writers whose early work will be built on in the future.

Thanks are due to the students' parents, all of whom gave their permission for their children to take part in the Thomas Hardy Creative

Workshops. They also gave their permission to have the resulting creative pieces published in this little book.

All the headteachers and one acting headteacher were very supportive of the creative sessions run in their schools. Each school section gives the name of the headteacher below the school's name.

The Thomas Hardy Creative Workshops would not have been possible without the tireless efforts of so many colleagues in each school. To them go sincerest thanks for arranging the sessions, ensuring that there were sufficient copies of the Thomas Hardy Creative Workshop Booklets, providing all the necessary stationery and laptops, and ensuring that all participants were well watered and nourished throughout the time of the Workshops. The persons to whom gratitude is due are: Nick Kelly (Teacher of English at Bryanston School), Rob Murray (Faculty Lead at Dorchester Middle School), Charlotte Hammond (Head of English at Greenwood Academy), Mark Chutter (Head of English at Dorset Studio School), Anna February-Perring (Year Tutor at St Osmund's Church of England Middle School), Leslie Allard (Teaching Assistant at Southlands School), Rachael Logsdon (Deputy Head of Faculty at The Taunton Academy) and Rachel Glennie (Head of English at The Thomas Hardye School).

Thanks are also due to Andrew Hewitt – Student Representative at The Thomas Hardy Society. He kindly submitted the four poems in the last section from Grace Bellorine and Similce Jacobson of The Woodroffe School in Lyme Regis, Emma Boddy of Mayfield School in Portsmouth and Esme Houghton-Oliver of Newton Abbot College in Newton Abbot. Andrew also obtained the necessary permissions for the publication of the four creative pieces in this book.

Rose Day generously gave permission for her poems to be published. These poems were composed during her recent tenure as Writer in Residence at Max Gate.

Samima Parvin has kindly allowed her sketch of Thomas Hardy to adorn the cover of this little Anthology. Samima completed her MA in English at the Diamond Harbour Women's University in Sarisha, West Bengal. She plans to carry out doctoral research in the near future. She is currently in Kolkata (India) working freelance on cover-designing projects.

The Editor is deeply grateful to Tim and Julie Musk of Roving Press for their unparalleled services. They were both generous with their advice on many aspects of this work. Julie and Tim were very patient in editing the photographs and illustrations submitted – especially in improving the quality of those where the originals were not available to the Editor.

Members of The Thomas Hardy Society Council of Management were supportive and encouraging all through the academic year 2019–2020. Particular thanks go to members of The Thomas Hardy Academic Sub-committee for their unstinting practical support and encouragement: Dr Tracy Hayes, Andrew Hewitt, Dr Karin Koehler, Dr Jonathan Memel, Andrew Leah and Marilyn Leah. The Chairman of The Thomas Hardy Society has always been encouraging, supportive and helpful.

As ever, members of the Thomas Hardy Poetry Group run by Helen Gibson continued to take an interest in the students' work. Many of them contributed positive commentary on poems shared with them over the academic year.

Every effort has been made to thank all those kind persons who have contributed so generously with their time, help, advice and support in producing this little volume. If any omissions have been made there was no discourtesy intended whatsoever. Readers who spot such shortcomings are invited to contact The Thomas Hardy Society on info@hardysociety.org.

Preface

I Look Into My Glass
Thomas Hardy

I look into my glass,
And view my wasting skin,
And say, 'Would God it came to pass
My heart had shrunk as thin!'

For then, I, undistrest
By hearts grown cold to me,
Could lonely wait my endless rest
With equanimity.

But Time, to make me grieve,
Part steals, lets part abide;
And shakes this fragile frame at eve
With throbbings of noontide.

This Anthology contains almost one hundred creative pieces. Last year, *Inspired by Thomas Hardy – An Anthology of Students' Poems 2019* contained 134 poems. This year's school visits to run the Thomas Hardy Creative Workshops were stopped after the last visit in mid-March 2020, when schools were closed until further notice owing to coronavirus. Thereafter, a few poems were still sent in by e-mail from various students or their teachers.

All creative responses are presented as they were submitted by the young writers who were promised that their voice would be respected. As happened in the highly successful 2019 Workshops, participants were also given the following three principles underlying all the Workshops:

(1) 'There is no good poetry or bad poetry: there is only self-expression within a free and mutually supportive group.' The same applies to all other creative responses.

(2) 'Composing a poem could be quite artificial and does not need a muse to propel the poet forward.' This underlying principle also applies to all other creative responses submitted.

(3) 'Poets can take whatever liberties they wish in using poetic licence when adapting, rewriting or borrowing from the poems and prose extracts shared with them.' Again, this 2019 underlying principle applied to all creative responses.

The best persons to introduce the works in this book are the students participating in the Creative Workshops. Harry Hubbard, Oscar Hills and JJ Sawtell from St Osmund's Church of England Middle School in Dorchester wrote the following:

'Today we read a collection of poems and prose pieces by Thomas Hardy and various other writers. We analysed several pieces, looking into the surface, and then deeper, meanings. We greatly enjoyed these activities and finished off by writing the following poems which you will read in this special book. We thank The Thomas Hardy Society and Faysal Mikdadi for giving us this special opportunity.'

Verity Mallinson, also from St Osmund's Church of England Middle School and whose poem 'Diamond Dust' appears in this book, wrote as follows:

'The Workshop was very helpful to inspire me to write my own poem. I have also read some poems by Thomas Hardy who I thought was an excellent poet. Reading him helped me to understand some poetic techniques. We also evaluated some poems by other poets as well as prose extracts such as the one from Frankenstein. Writing my own poem at the end was great fun, and throughout the Workshop we learned about different poets and their ways of speaking to us. Thank you to Faysal Mikdadi and to all the students who took part in this Workshop.'

Other students were positive in their judgements of the Creative Workshops, with the following few samples representing the overall responses:

- 'I have never been able to find inspiration. Now I feel confident writing a poem.'
- 'It was a lot of fun. More interesting than a normal lesson because we were being creative and felt in control.'
- 'More learning through understanding of poetry which helped us get into writing without being judged.'
- 'Most literature that we normally do is irrelevant. This is us. This is real.'
- 'Amazing. Love it. I was never a great fan of poetry … but I am now.'
- 'Poetry is enjoyable and thought provoking.'
- 'I was always scared of writing poetry. A lot of today's poems are tacky and embarrassing. I did not want to write like that. Hardy and the others show me that I can be a serious writer. Now I have the courage to write.'

The Afterword at the end of this book gives a brief description of the workshops. It also includes an abridged draft of the *Thomas Hardy School Creative Workshops 2020 Schemes of Work* and the bespoke edition of the Southlands School – the *Thomas Hardy School Creative Workshops 2020 Students' Booklet*.

The credit for this collection of students' creative responses goes to the students and their teachers. The Editor takes responsibility for any inadvertent shortcomings. Readers are welcome to point out any such shortcomings by sending a brief e-mail to info@hardysociety.org, whose responsible members would ensure that future editions are accordingly amended.

Faysal Mikdadi
Academic Director of The Thomas Hardy Society
Dorchester, 2020

National Trust Max Gate
Writer in Residence Summer 2019
Rose Day

Extract from **The Darkling Thrush**
Thomas Hardy

I leant upon a coppice gate
When Frost was spectre-grey,
And Winter's dregs made desolate
The weakening eye of day.
The tangled bine-stems scored the sky
Like strings of broken lyres,
And all mankind that haunted nigh
Had sought their household fires.

Rose Day is a British student and poet. She is currently completing a Doctorate of Philosophy in Creative Writing at the University of Exeter.

Her thesis is on the Eco-Gothic in Contemporary Literature.

Rose's research interests include contemporary fiction, nature writing and poetry with visual art.[6]

As from the 25 March 2020, Rose Day has been nominated for the Jane Martin Poetry Prize 2020.

---

[6] More of Rose Day's creative output may be read on the following sites:
rosed.squarespace.com
instagram.com/rosedaywrites/
@cloverandwhite
cloverandwhite.wordpress.com

Poems composed at Max Gate by Rose Day

Emma's Attic or/
Yours always, H
Rose Day

He paces with a soft foot
Little figure, his head slung low
I wonder what he sees in the roots, the soil
What poetry is there in the moss beneath?

There is something in the light of my garden,
Its tender warmth, feathered upon his neck
The strange, enticing scent of rosemary
Its pine, dropping from the stem

Somewhere in the house, the piano plays
A song half remembered,
In the redemption of spring
Somewhere in the house, another sings

The window conceals the glow of the fire
Against the skin of my lips, the tilt of my chin
For a moment, his head turns upwards
As though he can remember my breath

But it is only the breeze, whispering sweetness
Dissipating under his hat. The melody below falters
He returns to his footsteps, a dogged two step
And the walls of my sanctuary crumble,

As the tread of footsteps breaks into the garden
The moment no longer ours, I turn to the desk,
With one last look to the sky, my papers flutter
As the music fades to the familiar melody of silence

Tess or/
The second study
Rose Day

I thought I knew about the end of things
Until it was the scratch of the pen, the smell of ink
The bronze glint of a lamp in the evening
The glimpse of turning leaves above my head

I thought I knew about poetry
Until it was in her red lips,
Her imperfect curve of an unreal figure
The red marks upon my fingers

I thought I knew about creation
Until it was the alcove, dappled in morning glow,
The voice that remained in my mind
Far after I put my pages to rest

I thought I knew about spirit
Until it was in the divinity of the ghost
Wandering through my door
Shaking her dark locks in affection

I thought I knew how to love
Until she came alive in my little red room
The rain arrived in gushes and accents
And I lost my heart to her once again

The 7th of March 1870 or/
The Poetry Study
Rose Day

What makes a relic?
The question lies in the wood
The markings of grief in mahogany drawers

This room, the unexamined periphery
Locked up from prying eyes, somewhere
Echoes the faint scent of sea dew, a thudding of hooves

Of course, it lies in the poetry
What else could contain her? The rubble of memory
Scattered upon the desk, unfixable, unfathomable

Words fail, she is the gaps in between my thoughts
The spiralling smoke below, her laugh –
Flying in the embers of the bonfire

Is it possible she can exist in another place?
Somewhere outside these red walls
In the ticking of the clock

O poetry, holding grief and absence captive
Will she survive outside of this room?
Will she return to the sapphire sea?

Lonely and absent,
Without a word for me?

The dining room or/
Tryphena rests
Rose Day

Morning breaks. The clink of teaspoons upon china cups and a rustling of skirts. The dog gnaws upon the rugs below. There is a body in the dining room.

Her eyelids raise lazily

'Ah, bonjour le cousin'

I sit. Nudge the wiry fur by my feet. The maid pours my tea. The body laughs.

I answer questions. The fire will be lit. The shutters will be closed. The silverware polished.

The body sighs.

'Don't you know me cousin?'

The cats slink across the floor, the soft bellies dragging before settling into slumbers.

'Shall we practice again?'

The piano plays, somewhere in the recess of the house, a fire is being turned.

She lounges upon the scroll arm, soft smile playing upon her lips. One arm draped upon her stomach.

'Yes, Tryphena, always.'

The drawing room or

cont ...

The last performance

Fingers spring upon the keys,
Melodies of sorrow, songs of grace
summoning dancing ladies, lonely hums.

Outside, the cobwebs are lacing the panes
Hanging in glistening strings.
There is a howling wave in the note,

Every song, dances, drifts and waltzes
Tripping flawlessly over itself
The music of Cornwall, clear and sea swept,

Revived, saturating the armchairs,
Swirling through the doors.
The greatest show of her life,

Dorchester, green and pleasant disappears.
Vanished to the music, the melody of the night,
In its place, a ballroom of feathered dress.

There will be no audience, that much is known
The notes are quietening now, drifting asleep
The quick fingered playing slows

Now it is a leisurely running stream, the hop
Of the sparrow, the settling bird on the branch
The melodies are fading into silence

O let there be an encore!
Let the songs continue far into the night
Let the inevitable hold for one more song

Alas the last note falls
like the last leaf of winter
leaving only the clunk of the piano lid

and the songs played no more

The kitchen or/
A Sprinkle of Sugar
Rose Day

Plump sweet apples baking
The cook's song, stirring, stirring
Rough hands knead the dough
Billows of snowy flour spiralling upwards

O the joy of a full kitchen, chattering
Singing, laughing with busy hands
The warm smell of mutton stew
Rising pastries softening

And in the wintertime
The rousing of the pudding
Ceremony of bubbling soup
Spitting fat of the bacon in the pan

The day is quick footsteps up the stairs
The slop of water in jugs, creating tide lines
The day was red hands, aflame with suds
The day will be aching bones and brittle nails

Consider this my last testament, this house
Belongs to no man, no tight-lipped executor,
No pile of faded papers on a mahogany desk
No church, no god, no winding family tree

O no this belongs to the invisible hands
That weave and scrub and sew and carry
And hold the life of Max Gate in their palms

The Helpmate of a Genius or/
The Master Bedroom
Rose Day

When winter came, the leaves stuck to the windows
Steadfast against the dashing rain, blurring the outside
He has been writing since the early hours
And I am becoming translucent, disappearing in strokes

The bedroom is too small and desperately big
I can hear her voice in the scatterings of paper
The slinking movements of the cats
Curling themselves around the doorways

Do you remember the train? The power of it?
The centre of the universe shifting, and your strange look
Puzzled by my unflinching eyes, wide and unquestioning
Watching me dance through the crowds of Liverpool Street

But you are no longer there, called back in grief
To the faint blue shores of a love misremembered
Immortalised in language, my own voice lost
In the spaces between his words and mine

The Room or/
First Study
Rose Day

She can almost believe that somewhere, in the wheat
fields of Dorset,
He sits. To watch the hedgerows, touch the blooming
border flowers
Stop occasionally to watch the clouds pass by slowly

Somewhere, his feet are light amongst the lavender
The pollen dances above his cheek
The rustle of a beloved's skirt behind him
Against the gentle coo of the wood pigeon

Somewhere there is another Dorset,
Another cottage tucked into the trees
That he returns to, when the dusk settles
Upon the stone artefact of his youth

Until then, she waits, soundlessly walking
Through the empty corridors, once bright
Hear the familiar clunk of a typewriter
Echo through the landing

Until then, she draws into the shadows,
Her large luminous eyes deadened
Against the soft pattering of grief
Held fast in memorial

Until then, she disappears into the crowds
Watches the train leave, listlessly
Traces the lines he left her to read
And sends his heart back to the sea

The alley of bending boughs or/
The Garden
Rose Day

Twisting privets line the lonely boughs
Each bushel brimming with the fruits of spring
Lining the outskirts of the house are the trees
Brimming with woodpeckers and noisy nut hatch

Once descending the house into shade
Now, a protective ring of ancient thicket
Encircles the land, blocking the view of prying eyes
Their duty served, they remain faithful to the cause

Deep below the bones lie, an unknown man
Left in the rich soil, kept safe in legacy
A fragility that lay small in their hands.
The lost bones of another life, nameless

Away from the cramped corridors of the house
The garden remains, sanctuary from racketing trains
To hold the wandering ghosts
That once watched the beeches rise

Bryanston School
Blandford Forum – Dorset

Headteacher: Mark Mortimer

A Church Romance
(Mellstock *circa* 1835)
Thomas Hardy

She turned in the high pew, until her sight
Swept the west gallery, and caught its row
Of music-men with viol, book, and bow
Against the sinking sad tower-window light.

She turned again; and in her pride's despite
One strenuous viol's inspirer seemed to throw
A message from his string to her below,
Which said: 'I claim thee as my own forthright!'

Thus their hearts' bond began, in due time signed.
And long years thence, when Age had scared Romance,
At some old attitude of his or glance
That gallery-scene would break upon her mind,
With him as minstrel, ardent, young, and trim,
Bowing 'New Sabbath' or 'Mount Ephraim'.

Box pews in
St Andrew's Church,
Winterborne Tomson.

Response to 'The Frozen Greenhouse'
Luca Allies

Delicate gentle curves become vulgar,
Fold of rosy pink skin roll slowly over,
Lost beneath sheets of white land green,
Two dainty legs, touching, never seen.
Separated by only the tension in the air,
Yet still beneath the surface joined by a hair.
Rooted and bound, locked without a key,
The love between two roses,
It's no different to that of you and me.

Untitled
Ivor Davies

Blemishes lain on a bone white face
Made frail by the attentive glow of a peaking ray
Through dust and over crystal sheets,
Young tones change into time stricken greys,
Shallow orange and yellow haze.

Tired pages held ink few recall,
Framed by corners etched with hardening lines,
Which climb through crimson stone which often whines
With unnoticed gasps to tired sighs
Long made blind are its emblazoned eyes.

The Self-Unseen
Izzy Fowley

We spend hours and hours every day,
Wishing and pushing the time away.
You're looking forward to what there is to come,
It becomes difficult to remember what you've just done.

Each minute seems to keep flashing by,
The newest thing there to catch your eye.
Right now seems sad and tired and boring,
But tomorrow you promise you'll be out exploring.

Don't let it pass you by unseen,
Just because tomorrow you'll finally be keen.
It's too easy to lose sight of what you've got,
You don't want to be the one to say you forgot.

Summer Days
Angelica Masters

Oh, how hard
It is to be
Someone joyous
and someone free

Yet, all day
The sun does smile
letting me feel
free for a while

In the light
Under the trees
the dappled shade
shelters my knees

Till the beams
Of light to fade
I stop and think
How was all made?

Life on earth
Fill up my brain
For both the beauty
And the pain

I really try
to treasure each day
As if it were my last
With no more to say

Mou Wàho / The Stupid Wèka
George Radley

On a small island in the South Pacific
There is a large lake
On this lake
There is a small island
On this island
There is a smaller lake and,
On this lake an even smaller island is situated.

A single tree stands on this island
Barely large enough to support a feather
Yet a tree stands there, natural and strong.

On the shore of the smallest lake
A bush compiled of diverse and distinct flora
Ferns known only to this land
Some curled up and Kelly green[7]
Others broad and brown
The darkness is all consuming,
As if the sun had been shut down.

A mystical silence fills the air,
A tropical plateau no life and no sound.
But if you would just put your ear to the ground and hear
A scratch and a squawk
From the island's only occupier.

It has the shape and colour
Of a small sack of potatoes
But a mighty crimson red, hooked beak.
Its search is irregular yet tireless
For its one juicy prey.

cont ...

---

[7] 'A bright, strong green colour' (*Cambridge Dictionary*).

The Weta[8] hides in and under logs
The soil and the sand
Rare and allusive yet a fine meal
For its fellow inhabitant
The stupid Weka[9]

Both supposedly evolved
Yet lost the ability to fly
Purposely disconnected from humanity
For the sake of their lives
Imprisoned together, only one left to breed in plethora.

---

[8] 'A New Zealand rodent-sized insect' https://www.sciencemag.org.
[9] 'The weka is one of New Zealand's iconic large flightless birds' (*New Zealand Birds*).

The Afflictions of Men
Angus Sherriff

You took my money
The money went with the food
And that insolent, sterile man
I hate him
Look what you've done to him, I say
'He is dead', death replies
Dead inside I suppose
Sadness engulfed him
We did not see the papers coming
They were just words
'Breakfast' he said
'Breakfast and tears'

Nature
Finlay Tedford

On sombre heights
a palace green
lives he whose
feeble hand
and sombre sheen
once had the mien
of mastery.

Now in his age and eye
wet things do dry
for death too reaps the tears he cries.

Untitled
Maddy Weatherby

Fatal rosy retrospect
emblazones on my eyes
what we both once knew for sure
fate had doomed to die.

Now all engulfed in celestial glow,
Suspended by a hovering cloud in the sky
The radiance of a perished past,
Spoils the clarity of my mind's eye.

We dwell in a sun drenched hollow,
Shadows cast by glorious days in June.
But of these we had none;
Yet they shroud my today,
With ineffable gloom.

In response to 'The Captive Dove'
Wilf Wheeler

What fragmented blurry haze of conjunct recollection,
What ugly creature that sings so sound,
A vial of tears,
To please foreign ears.
Stripped naked on page,
Not granted age.
Scars bound in time, structure, rhythm and rhyme.

*'Painting on wood' of William Barnes by Pete Sheridan
(with permission from owner Faysal Mikdadi).*

Dorchester Middle School

Dorchester – Dorset

Acting Headteacher: Caroline Pluck

The Difference
Thomas Hardy

I

Sinking down by the gate I discern the thin moon,
And a blackbird tries over old airs in the pine,
But the moon is a sorry one, sad the bird's tune,
For this spot is unknown to that Heartmate of mine.

II

Did my Heartmate but haunt here at times such as now,
The song would be joyous and cheerful the moon;
But she will see never this gate, path, or bough,
Nor I find a joy in the scene or the tune.

It's a Year Almost
Beatrice Clifford

it's a year almost that I've seen,
the sky blue and the grasses green.
I no longer see the way, that butterflies
dance … and soar and play.

no more do I live and breathe,
… the pain and ache my heart receives.
I can not again see the sun,
the deed of death cannot be undone.

I miss the smell of freshly baked bread,
the silk of a pillow against my head.
I miss the days when I was free,
but the deed of death is upon me.

Sunlight
Jasmine Coman-Miller

Trees, silent, motionless and still,
They patiently wait until,
The sun has come to shine
Glistening through the end of time.

To just feel the comfort of its warmth … of its rays,
Touch the tips of your fingers or the very end of your nose,
You feel perfect, in so many new ways,
The sunlight has the beauty of a flower … a rose.

Burning, shining a million miles up in the sky,
You just want to reach, look and fly,
For there is no feeling like the kiss of the sun,
You feel joy, pride, sunlight and fun.

Old Oak Tree
Seren Daly

The door slams shut
and footsteps echo,
where music played
where laughter shadowed

But now the beams are bruised and battered
the vines that twine,
are carefully flattened
the squirrels scurry in the leaves
no crackling fire to warm their feet
no calls of joyful smiles meet

But only the groan of an old oak tree
which during night continues to speak
the tree that welcomes stars back home
in midnight and daylight and winter snow

While white flowers grow on greying tiles
that droop and loom in vibrant towers
as yellow buzzes
and pigeons chatter
in sunlight, and when that is gone
they journey all the way back home
to see their family crawl and grow
forgetting, over time, that day
where branches sheltered them from storms
and kept them safe and dry and warm

But it does not forget the sight
of birds that chattered in the night
or buzzing bees and falling leaves
nor flowers falling or chicks calling
in branches, in the old oak tree

The Captive Tiger
Daisy Flux
(Inspired by Anne Brontë's The Captive Dove*)*

Poor restless tiger, I pity him:
Prowling up and down behind those bars.
His magnificent colours, his sharp claws.
They were not made for this!
He looks at me with those deep blue eyes of his
And asks me a thousand questions,
To which I cannot reply.
Then he looks away, and into the distance
No doubt dreaming of times long ago.
When trees stood tall;
When birds cried out in wonderful melodies.
Times when he was free: so free.

But then I looked deeper into those eyes.
And a whole other story I saw.
One of horror, destruction and death,
Of loss, fear and flames.
All reflected in those whiny, almost tearful, memory voids.
Oh tiger, you could 'melt a heart harder than mine'.

What do you see in my eyes, tiger?

After I found you
Charlotte Amy Gale

After I found you,
My heart was aglow.
When I was with you,
I never felt low.
You said you wouldn't leave me.
You said would let go.
The day that you left me,
The sky was grey and the rain was aflow.
Thunder all around me all of that day.
I never knew the feeling of being broken in that way.
After I lost you my heart shattered.
I lost my beautiful cat that day.
My cat has now gone away.

Some Time Ago
Elian Hallett

Looking back, some time ago,
I wonder what I didn't know,
I think of all the blissful years,
Joy and laughter, free of tears.

Aromatic flowers, smelling sweet,
Rolling fields full of wheat,
Flowing rivers, stepping stones,
Eating jam and cream with scones.

Wriggling my toes within the sand,
Feeling the joining of sea, sky and land,
The crashing waves, the endless sea,
I loved the past, and it loved me.

Yet it's all gone now, it won't come back,
In fun and joy, life forever lacks,
The candle of life, now melting away,
Never waste a single day.

Behold the ancient story
Declan McDermott

Behold, the ancient story
Of young men, destined for glory.
If you break trust with us who fought,
Your long-lived soul will not rest one thought.

Victory but not for cowards like you,
For our nation, then you shall be punished too.
Severe consequences if you disrespect what we aspire
Will be given to those who perceive us as liar.

Strive to be part of the deeper,
We must continue marching, steeper.
Don't let us down – don't let us die
When it's all over … oh my … oh my.

There is the ancient tapestry
Alexander Mistry-Dyer

There is the ancient tapestry
worn, torn and frayed
there is the forgotten tomb
where many memories were made.

I remember the men, who fought the battle
to protect this castle, and all the cattle
I remember the men that didn't survive
the ones who have lost their lives.

In a trance, I walked up the stairs
and looked out the window at the top of the tower
and there I saw
the flowers.

The Lonely Raft
Kitty Short

The lonely raft floating on the ocean,
Memories come flooding back quicker, quicker,
The salty spray splashing my face,
Deep in thought of this empty place.

The song of a seagull,
The crash of a wave,
Makes me calmer, calmer in every way.

Rays of golden sun glance through the clouds,
I stare into your eyes deeper, deeper,
Pools of water innocent and sweeter.

As the clouds hide away,
The day is done,
'Worries, doubt, fears, when counted are none'.[10]

---

[10] Line borrowed from 'The Beach' by Charlotte Parkes, page 62, Mikdadi, Faysal (Editor), *Inspired by Thomas Hardy – An Anthology of Students' Poems 2019*, published by Roving Press for The Thomas Hardy Society, Dorchester, 2019.

When you're gone
Evie White

When you're gone,
the sky is grey,
the children have gone silent
no longer out to play.

It was the day I went to school,
I kissed you goodbye and so by rule,
I left to go on the bus with glee,
not knowing that you were going to be taken away from me.

My day of learning went on and on,
we learnt a new type of happy song,
but little did I know behind my back,
you were being laid, your heart attack.

I got home, I sat down, but rose for a sound,
I found my mother crying there,
standing, staring at the chair.

Upon this chair I found a necklace lying there.
I felt my eyes welling with tears, as I
saw the note, it said:

'Goodbye my friend I shall miss you,
but don't cry, just remember me.'
From your faithful dog.

Max Gate, Hardy's home.

Dorset Studio School
Dorchester – Dorset
Headteacher: Annetta Minard

The Sun on the Bookcase
(Student's Love-Song: 1870)
Thomas Hardy

Once more the cauldron of the sun
Smears the bookcase with winy red,
And here my page is, and there my bed,
And the apple-tree shadows travel along.
Soon their intangible track will be run,
And dusk grow strong
And they have fled.

Yes: now the boiling ball is gone,
And I have wasted another day ...
But wasted – wasted, do I say?
Is it a waste to have imagined one
Beyond the hills there, who, anon,
My great deeds done,
Will be mine alway?

The Frost
Sam Cartwright
(Inspired by Thomas Hardy's The Frozen Greenhouse)

The ice glazed the window
It covered the lake also
The flowers frozen in time
And I was sat inside

The fire roared and raged
Warming up the little room
The coffee sat steaming on the table
The sun shone through the window

In here it was warm
Out there it was cold
The world's a contrast
Warm inside: outside a cold blast.

One Must Want
Maddie Damon

As one to love
another must fight
but some will loathe
these who flight
others will watch and stand by
as others will act and take sides
those who won't will turn green
when the rest will accept and then gleam

Blanket of White
Megan Elliott

A mesmerising blanket of white
A town buzzing with life
A mystical magical sight
What a time to be alive

Snowflakes shining in the light
Icicles hanging from heights
A cold frosty morning bite
What a time to be alive

Fake
Thomas Horsington

My eyes fixed within a mesmerising trance.
As trees sway in the wind like drunken men.
The whistling winds to which long grass dance.
While curs' cubs awaken from inside their den.

The sun stands above me bearing bright beams of light.
For while I stand here nothing could cause me fright.
With glitters of light shimmering on the lake
I think to myself was it all just a dream? Fake.

Mother
Heather House
(Inspired by Christina Rossetti's A Bird Song*)*

'It's a year almost that I have not seen her'
we've always been together.
through thick and thin.
mother and daughter.

the fight became unbearable.
sisters ruined what we had.
the oldest became an adult.
no childhood of her own.

'It's a year almost that I have not seen her'
let's keep it this way.

Dreams
Caitlin Killeen

There they stand;
The Dreamer;
And anything is possible.
There they stand;
The Dreamer;
And a world lives at their feet;
People and lives unknown;
Monsters from tales, faces from life;
Half-recollections of memories long gone.
There they stand, the Dreamer;
And the story grows around them;
Adventure and mystery;
Excitement and love;
There they stand;
The Dreamer;
And anything is possible.

Love is a treasure
Carlisle M
(*Inspired by Anne Brontë's* The Captive Dove)

Love is a treasure.
It comes in many forms.
Just like the sun it's bright and warm.
Love has many beautiful colours.
The forms of love are captivating like a pure dove
who brings peace.
Love is a purity not a sin to feel for the same gender
or both.
Love who you wish … We won't judge you for it.
Most lovers' embrace is warm and full of kindness.
Other lovers' embraces are full of passion, beauty
and meaning.

Love is a treasure.

Him
Mary-Anne Martin

I walked through the door
and saw him again
I see and hear him everywhere
we joke and laugh together

deep down I knew better
she was better for him than I
but he did not like her
no! he liked me just for me

they sat behind a frosty window
looking like they were trying to make a decision
later I found out it was a surprise
arranging a week in Paris just for me …

Goodbye
Katelyn Peadon

I saw her standing there
summer's short breeze blowing
Through her long dark hair

the starry sky
reflected in her eye
so much more
for us to explore

the birds that soared overhead
singing their good night song
they dived and flipped
so free to fly

How I wish I didn't have to say goodbye.

Come to me
Richard Phillips
(Inspired by Shelley's To a Skylark *and Thomas Hardy's*
Shelley's Skylark*)*

come to me for a prophecy,
to he who knows all,
had much to see,
come to me before the fall,
let us meet by the sea.

come to me for a view of fate,
he who knows of woe and lust,
he who understands your hate,
invest in me your immortal trust,
let us talk of what will happen late.

come to me for your future,
something clear that only he knows,
I can be like a tutor,
someone only he shows,
I'll be a teacher.

come to me for your immortality,
give me your patience each day,
and let heaven think of you thoughtfully,
he who doesn't patronise in any way,
come to me and find out what you ought to be.

if you seek the powers of a God,
come down and visit,
step out of the fog you're enveloped in,
and join in on this new age; join with it;
be a part of it.

Bedroom at Max Gate.

Greenwood Academy
Birmingham – West Midlands

Headteacher: Allen Bird

The Voice
Thomas Hardy

Woman much missed, how you call to me, call to me,
Saying that now you are not as you were
When you had changed from the one who was all to me,
But as at first, when our day was fair.

Can it be you that I hear? Let me view you, then,
Standing as when I drew near to the town
Where you would wait for me: yes, as I knew you then,
Even to the original air-blue gown!

Or is it only the breeze, in its listlessness
Travelling across the wet mead to me here,
You being ever dissolved to wan wistlessness,
Heard no more again far or near?

Thus I; faltering forward,
Leaves around me falling,
Wind oozing thin through the thorn from norward,
And the woman calling.

December 1912

The Game
Anonymous[11]

I am interested in Games. You are not sure why the
word 'Game' starts with a capital G. It is because the
people who created the computer game had created
their own world – their own thing: The Game.
Minecraft is my favourite survival game. I like it
because there is always an extra thing no matter
how much time I spend playing it. The game grows
all the time – a sense of electricity gives it new life
like Professor Frankenstein's poor Creature. It is a
solitary game and I like my own Company.

---

[11] This piece was dictated by a student who wished to remain anonymous. Faysal
Mikdadi scribed it as dictated during the time that was devoted to allow students
to create whatever response they wished after sharing a selection of poetry and
prose.

where you once played golf, is now just a golf-course
madison louise joan barrett

before
christmases held joy
autumn just a happy season,
i didn't realise time would slip by
so fast.
every second
assumed to last forever.
now a lot of things seem empty.
well, not empty, maybe just less whole.
i wish i could go back
life used to be so carefree

now
christmas has lost joy, autumn too
because it lost happy, it lost you
no longer remains the feeling of
will you walk through the door?
as the reality hits
you are not here anymore

The one that lived
Grace Dalley

Here where you would sit,
guitar in hand
and where you'd be
for hours on end.
Your well known presence
Only now rests in the form
Of an empty chair.
Yet, we bring alive your memory,
to us you are still here.

The light may have dimmed.
but the candle still burns.
Representing warmth I once had
but no longer submerge my troubles within
though our hearts droop heavy with absence,
we are content with your peace.
And now go on to dream on such a scale
once done by you.

You were here
You lived
You loved, and were loved.

Good night to you.
The one that lived.

25/3/18
Scarlett Dempsey

I was in a dream
But not too deep
The moment when my dream became a reality
Which involved fatality.
I dreamt about a single soul
One I had recognised
One that I had seen once before my eyes.
This was a reality I did not want to realise.

ran without a trace
was this really their fate
The fault lies in their hands.
my hope would be that this was
Something unplanned.

Time Passing
Kate Horden

Tick tock another hour passed by,
another day passes,
another month passes,
but things don't numb.

No colour looks the same,
no food tastes the same,
even the sun doesn't shine as brightly,
When will this end?

Tick tock, another month passes by,
things are still the same,
Nothing has changed.

The albion
Oscar Rock

the sun beams down on the hawthorns
thousand in attendance
Screaming bomber drowns name
beers have been drunk
burgers have been scoffed
it's time to start singin
with arms and Scuses[12] aloft
This is the albion.

---

[12] Urban or slang expression usually used as an obnoxious or loud interjection meaning 'excuse me'.

Death before death
Joseph Room

mind and body opposed to thought are not amalgamated;
the mind dies before the body rots.
memories of life are cruel, life isn't life. life
is a fire in the cycle of deprivation of cinders.

God is a farce fires rage on mortal land
as a citadel collapses killing its residents who
deceive themselves that things happen because of
God's plan

Death is a sickness. No life is a sickness that all minds
Share.
We share that we are born to die.
Death is just when the feather hits the ground
memory is torture

memory is the blade that ruptures the mind, heart and
leaves the body a wasting corpse.

Dove in the rain
Lexi Smith

Sitting on my window sill,
guilt takes over my mind.
Obsessing over memories,
as I stare into its eyes.
It looks back at me blankly,
With raindrops on its sides.

So pure, so honest.
Probably never broken a promise,
probably never told a lie,
from the innocence conveyed in its eyes.
No pain hidden behind them.

I sit there and watch as the rain falls upon it.
I could've let it in, I could've kept it warm.
Instead it's out there shivering,
begging for my help.

The rain then stops,
the dove takes off,
the memories then fade ...

Frozen in time
Paris Smith

Lying flat on my bed
Visioning nightmares in my head
I let out a booming scream
Yet nothing happens, was it all a dream?

The clock strikes 12, it's midnight again
How am I outside, why am I in pain?
Blood on my hands, is this what I spilt?
My mistakes are coming back, flooding me with guilt

The clock strikes 12, it's midnight again
My mind is puzzled, I feel insane
I'm holding a gun, but why might that be?
I'm frozen in time, wanting to be set free

The clock strikes 12, it's midnight again
The images I vision, why are they in my brain?
Is that really … no it can't be, you're dead!
I feel like I'm walking on thin ice, hanging by a thread

The clock strikes 12, it's midnight again …

My Only Memory
Cerys Tyers

No bad times
No good times
My only memory
No child-like dreams
No thoughts of the past
My only memory

In a haze, lights flashing
I wake up in confusion
All I can see
Nothing
My eyes close shut and my mind goes blank
My only memory
Still a blur

Steam train in the Purbeck.

St Osmund's
Church of England Middle School
Dorchester – Dorset

Headteacher: Saira Sawtell

At the Railway Station, Upway
Thomas Hardy

'There is not much that I can do,
        For I've no money that's quite my own!'
        Spoke up the pitying child –
A little boy with a violin
At the station before the train came in, –
'But I can play my fiddle to you,
And a nice one 'tis, and good in tone!'

        The man in the handcuffs smiled;
The constable looked, and he smiled, too,
        As the fiddle began to twang;
And the man in the handcuffs suddenly sang
        With grimful glee:
        'This life so free
        Is the thing for me!'
And the constable smiled, and said no word,
As if unconscious of what he heard;
And so they went on till the train came in –
The convict, and boy with the violin.

Shooting Stars
Adelaide Croucher

I stopped to stare at the night sky,
And wondered how it coped,
For when of my own would fall and die,
I should always lose hope,

Yet fall does its stars both day and night,
And still the sky does hold,
So when it does not plunder down,
My joy can still unfold.

Trapped
Adelaide Croucher

Oh dear small oak how I pity you,
With all your roots pulling you down,
And your poor soul searching for a clue,
That in your sorrow you shan't drown,

And your motionlessness restrains you,
From breathing out a single sound,
Though even if I myself can move,
I too am also restrained,

For in the eyes of many others,
My actions may seem strange.

Sunlit Haze
Tom Hadgett

I stare thoughtfully at the ground I tread,
An unearthly walk from beyond the grave,
Sunlight cuts darkness into nothing but shreds,
Yet in this playful sense I must behave.

The life I live has merely just begun,
In childhood, life is so serious,
However, life also seems so fun,
And childlike dreams make us delirious.

Family reunions for granted,
Now I am so free, just like a dove,
My life always seemed so slanted,
My heart so longs for my family's love.

And now I am at my family's grave,
Right now I know that I must be so brave.

Chaotic world
Oscar Hills

In this chaotic world,
There is little peace.
But when we go walking,
Some chaos does cease.

The golden rays,
From the sun up above.
And the everlasting song,
Of the beautiful dove.

The whistles in the trees,
From the wind blowing through.
And that childhood path,
Where walk I still do.

So even though some chaos may never seem to cease,
Down that country path, there is immortal peace.

'Country Lane' drawn by Oscar Hills.

A Memory
Harry Hubbard

She sits playing on the floor,
Laughter fills the room,
Happiness eradiating,
Memories in the making,

A small boy sits with her,
Sharing in her joy,
The moments passed so fast,
She is gone now,

But the memory stays,
Locked away in his mind,
Eternally,
For she is never truly gone.

Subconscious
Annie Lee

Gentle sunlight reaching down into
Rippling tufts of lime-green grass.
Sparkling diamond-water brook,
Embracing lonely blossoms, whose time has come to pass.

Twisted tree-trunk spiralling up out of the earth,
Sporting boughs of cherry-pink and rose.
It is here I sit, my thoughts afloat,
In my peaceful place, away from my woes.

Diamond Dust
Verity Mallinson

You can only smash a diamond
If you hit it with another,
Stronger,
Diamond.
It doesn't take a diamond
To break a heart.
It takes two hearts;
One strong,
One weak,
To turn it into diamond dust.
You can sellotape it together with 'I'm sorry'
But it will never be the diamond it used to be.

Promises
Evelyn Mason

In a cupboard under the stairs
A girl's bag sat waiting,
Safe inside were her promises
That had been lost but never taken,
The girl didn't need them anymore
For she had what she wanted,
She could see it whenever she wished
For it was all made up in her head.

Gleaming Spirit
Amelie Richardson

Tidal wave of grief consumes yet abandons me,
Leaving me to wonder in the darkness,
I did not know that what was inevitable,
Would soon unravel to be the hardest journey yet.

Mother much missed whilst gone but somehow still here,
Has not truly disappeared,
Joyous spirit is always around,
and shall forever be gleaming.

The Garden
JJ Sawtell

Rows of fire dancing along the sun-baked Earth.
Their embers igniting the dirt into terracotta.
The bare landscape a victim of the ever-burning fire.

The rows of citrus sting held high in rays of sun.
Their constant flames searing into the thick flesh of the fruit.
The juice, sharper than anything.

I sit here, alone, looking at the fruit and the flowers.

Barrow Lane, Corscombe (taken from Secret
Places of West Dorset *by Louise Hodgson).*

Southlands School
Lymington – Hampshire

Principal: Karen Gaster
Head of Education: Kelly McKay

The Frozen Greenhouse
Thomas Hardy
(St Juliot)

'There was a frost
Last night!' she said,
'And the stove was forgot
When we went to bed,
And the greenhouse plants
Are frozen dead!'

By the breakfast blaze
Blank-faced spoke she,
Her scared young look
Seeming to be
The very symbol
Of tragedy.

The frost is fiercer
Than then to-day,
As I pass the place
Of her once dismay,
But the greenhouse stands
Warm, tight, and gay,

While she who grieved
At the sad lot
Of her pretty plants –
Cold, iced, forgot –
Herself is colder,
And knows it not.

As the day went by, students, teachers and teaching assistants joined the group in increasing numbers. Five of the adults present wrote and shared their own pieces as a way of supporting and encouraging their students to have a go. One adult courageously confessed that she had never been too keen on poetry but that, after experiencing this Workshop, she had discovered a new love of poetry. The adults' pieces are printed after the students' contributions below.

Onyx
Morgan Gibbs

Pitch black dog I walk in the heart of night,
no stars no moon no nothing in sight,
a shadow chained, kept on a slide slack leash
will he break or will he keep?

Guarding our steps by shades unharmed
Do I walk him or does he walk me?

A speck of pale fear
where all else is swallowed.
the night carelessly holds my leash.

no longer is there a dog;
for the night has swallowed me.

Mary Channing's Boy

Morgan Gibbs

(Inspired by Thomas Hardy's Maumbury Ring
extract from his Personal Writings *and from a
brief extract from his* The Mayor of Casterbridge*)*

her son was a dead boy,
never had a real toy,
unless you count her fickle heart,
which tore itself apart,
from those righteous flames,
past the burning eyes.

he was a cold boy,
abandoned sickly boy,
Jesus reincarnate to the Virgin Mary of disgrace,
strung up on a wooden cross in distaste,
crucified for her sins
just for our entertainment whims.

Untitled
Morgan Gibbs
(Inspired by Thomas Hardy's The Self-Unseeing*)*

moths, flies, creeps and crawls,
six limbed angels with haloes spun aglow
in wings of gossamer
infinite eyes for these fragile lives
pride after all is a deadly sin
these humble creatures
are the only to be forgiven
simplicity in a way sinners
can't understand
so here we stand, giants in purgatory,
unknowingly with heaven's dearest
they are innocent, intricate
threes theology set in armour holy.

A Dove

Morgan Lowman

(Inspired by a discussion of memories of childhood –
happy and otherwise – after reading Thomas Hardy's
The Self-Unseeing*)*

It flies above
gently soaring through the skies
as it starts to wonder why
the world is so full of lies
why do people suffer
and force themselves to become tougher
there's so much wealth
yet people keep it for themselves
people suffer in silence
while others can only incite violence
if only the dove could help
but he was only small himself
the dove has always known
that love is not always shown
but he knew it was there
under the cover of despair

Untitled
Shannon O'Connor
(Inspired by Christina Rossetti's A Bird Song*)*

It's over a year I have not seen him
oh November 2018 things were greater than great
funner than fun, fewer than few
everything felt new too
a few months passed everyone gasped
I thought this would last
everything seemed fast

Manly Shannon
Shannon O'Connor
(in collaboration with Teaching Assistant Vicky Gaunt)

There was Vicky
her name was niki
She liked to be tricky
her bones were clicky
her finger were sticky
She liked to take the micky

Portrait of Thomas Hardy by James Turner.

a happy face is not all you are
because when you cry help is not far

'Mask of Happiness' drawn by Imogen Wheatley.

'Hardy Landscape' drawn by Grace Wilkinson.

'Bird' – photograph taken by Zachar Doney.

'Dorset' – *photograph taken by Zachar Doney.*

Childhood Days
Leslie Allard – Teaching Assistant
(Inspired by Thomas Hardy's The Self-Unseeing*)*

The childhood days,
When one learns and plays,
Are not always far from mind,
When over the years we look behind.

Those days show keen joy.
When perhaps we had that special toy!

We don't think of cares and strife,
That now become our path of life.

Now as a parent I see renewed,
The innocence of life, not to be subdued.

But as already has been said;
In a poem read before going to bed.
'What is life, if full of care,
We have no time to stop and stare?'[13]

---

[13] Lines quoted from Willian Henry Davies' poem 'Leisure'.

The House I Grew up in
Tom Fishwick – Teacher of English
(Inspired by Thomas Hardy's The Self-Unseeing*)*

The House I grew up in.
Someone else's now …
I pass it by sometimes,
Catching a sideways glance.
They painted the door. French Grey.
They built an extension.
The Grand House opposite demolished for flats.
Retirement living; where people go to die.

Yet when I dream I roam that House once more.
Sleepy footsteps wearing out the landing carpet.
My old bedroom behind a film of sub-consciousness
The kitchen clouded by a hypnotic glaze like
Steam from a cheerfully bubbling kettle.
That sip of hot tea curled up on the familiar
Leather with the familiar smell.
These mix in my mind until I am awake.
Stark contrast to my new world. Not a patch on the old.

Childhood
Crystal Irving – Head of English
(Inspired by Thomas Hardy's The Self-Unseeing)

The warmth of childhood sunshine.
Days that laugh and shine.
Never ending afternoons.
I am blessed that they are mine.
'Come home when the streetlights blaze.'
'Wash your hands before you eat.'
'Feed the dog and wash the car.'
Innocent, pink and sweet.

Darker days discovering that
Our naïve joy would wane.
The sadness of this knowledge
Smiling from a faded sepia frame.

The warmth of childhood sunshine.
Days that both blurred and shone.
Time twisting away
and running from us.
I remember
now they are gone.

Nonna and the Swallows
Manuela Zucchi – Teaching Assistant
(Inspired by Thomas Hardy's The Self-Unseeing*)*

It is an ordinary Tuesday, I am sitting here, in a room, at work, with adults, with children and much, much more.

As the lines of a poem are being read out, I am transported away, to a time and a place, far far away in my memory …

… walking down the road, on a hot summer afternoon, a young girl was holding hands with her grandmother. They were waiting for the cooler hours of the late afternoon to come and a short stroll helped to kill half an hour of another hot day.

When they arrived in front of the walls of a hay barn, grandma gazed upwards, looking with her eyes for something that she knew she would find. She reached up, right to wooden beams that supported the roof.

The warm air of the late summer afternoon was filled with the scent of delightful Jasmine but also with the even sweeter sense of anticipation.

Around the two figures, who stood on that spot, fast, black shadows were darting in all directions. The tiny girl looked at her grandmother as she whispered some soft words and pointed her stumpy index at a knobbly-looking, yellowish clump that sat just under the black wooden beams.

The sunlight was strong and the tiny girl could not keep her eyes open long enough to see against the sun. She held her palm over her brow and all of a sudden the relief of some shade allowed her eyes to adjust.

cont …

And the marvel of innocence left her mesmerised.

Grandma looked down as the little girl was still beaming with joy.

A very loud chirping echoed above their heads: four, no no wait, five, tiny beaks were poking out from the top of that strange clump. The chicks were so loud, calling out for their mum and dad to come back soon, to quench their thirst, to feed their hunger and calm their spirits.

The child and grandma saw how fast the parent birds returned to the nest to feed their young then departed again in a frenzy of wings fluttering.

'The swallows are here,' she said to the girl. 'They have returned to find their old nest and to bring new life.' The girl looked up at the old woman: 'They do that every year.'

Every year after that moment, on a hot summer day, the grandma and the girl stood there, on the very same spot, to admire that miracle of life. The girl grew taller and grandma older as the years went by. Until the year the girl returned to that place not with grandma, but holding her own children's hands, whilst she searched for these tiny beaks. She whispered the same words she was told when she was tiny – and as the swallows returned to their nests after the winter, she wished that her grandma could return too.

Burning at the Stake
Anonymous
(Inspired by Thomas Hardy's Maumbury Ring
extract from his Personal Writings *and by a brief*
extract from his The Mayor of Casterbridge*)*

Burning at the Stake!
Don't be late!

Cried the Town Cryer.
Here in Dorchester, not at the Tower!

Burning at the Stake!
Don't be late!

Shouting aloud.
Hustling the crowd

Mary Channing!
Not fit for hanging!

Burning at the Stake!
Don't be late!

Time she suffered for her treacherous fate!
Burning at the Stake!
Don't be late!

Poisoning her spouse,
While entertaining lovers in his house!

Burning at the Stake!
Don't be late!

The Grocer's wife,
Now forfeiting her life!

cont ...

Burning at the Stake!
Don't be late!

Flighty was she,
'though a Mother to be!

Burning at the Stake!
Don't be late!

Soon will be the Hour!
Cried the Town Cryer.

Burning at the Stake!
Don't be late!

Now in years gone by,
People they are asking, 'Why?'

If there was a reasonable doubt!
It was not heard above the shout!

Burning at the Stake!
Don't be late!

Mary Channing!
Not fit for hanging!

Received her punishment at the hands of Man.
Where was the redeemer to say, 'Throw the first
stone if You can!'

The Taunton Academy

Taunton – Somerset

Headteacher: Jenny Veal

An August Midnight
Thomas Hardy

I

A shaded lamp and a waving blind,
And the beat of a clock from a distant floor:
On this scene enter – winged, horned, and spined –
A longlegs, a moth, and a dumbledore;
While 'mid my page there idly stands
A sleepy fly, that rubs its hands ...

II

Thus meet we five, in this still place,
At this point of time, at this point in space.
– My guests besmear my new-penned line,
Or bang at the lamp and fall supine.
'God's humblest, they!' I muse. Yet why?
They know Earth-secrets that know not I.

Max Gate, 1899

Bedroom at Hardy's Cottage, Stinsford.

Love
Amy Bailey
(*Inspired by Thomas Hardy's* The Difference,
The Voice *and* The Frozen Greenhouse)

the one thing we all crave
the thing we hope will solve all our problems
We believe it will complete us
but when it's over
it leaves us more broken than when we started

We trust it is to save us
praying it will mend us
when in reality it's the
thing that ruins us

The Mask
Alexander Bulloso
(Inspired by Helen Maria Williams' Hymn Written among
the Alps *and Anne Brontë's* The Captive Dove*)*

You feel the weight fall off your shoulders
The midnight sky, white sparks scattered
Lying on grass, you don't feel colder
Else but a view like this, you'd crawl for the latter

The almost eerie deafening silence
A drop, a tear, falls down to the ground
For coming: anger, hatred, fatigue, violence
You don't want this night to end; the solitude keeps you sound

No one else knows you're here. Feel free to laugh and cry
To pander and laugh at memories, to weep for losses, not
they're all yours
But, to this safe haven, when you have to say good bye
Put on your mask, the man who you're not. Masked forced on
for hours

And when the mask falls, come running back to the place
The place where the sky flows to calm you down
And tear off your mask, reveal your humble face
For a void awaits, never filled with your rain
A paradise no-one knows, to laugh, to cry, to rejoice, to frown
Where judgment is non-existent, and there's no need to be
ashamed.

Midnight Adventures
Mara Garang and Abi King

I go to the window at midnight,
Lay my hand on her head.
Beside her bed a flickering light,
As she rests peaceful in bed.

I take her hand in mine,
She awakes with an innocent look.
As she realises it's her time,
She remembers me from the book.

We make our way to the window,
Pirates and mermaids to show.
Be sure not to fly too low,
Off to Neverland we go!

Angels
Ellie Govier and Maddie White
(Inspired by Thomas Hardy's The Difference*)*

She will go to the heavens soon,
where she will dance with the angels,
and sing with the doves,
but she will never see the luminous moon again,

Although her golden locks are gone,
Her eyes still glisten,
Her smile still warm,
but she will never hear her favourite song again,

The wind took her away,
like a boat on a long voyage,
the pain is gone and she can rest,
but he will never see her teddy bear again,

She sits in the clouds happy and content,
Now a star in the sky,
Knowing
she's loved forever and always.

Silence
Jack Guns

Silence filled the empty room
Middle of the night with the moon
This old house was left derelict
I stood alone until it clicked

I remember living here
Back when I had no tears
With all my family
We all lived out by the sea

I try to remember the good times
When my life didn't depend on the roll of someone else's die

A View from a Window
Tommy Hallows

Pale white sky,
Grass lay undisturbed,
Branches of trees hung low.

The world stood motionless in isolation,
Not a single sign of devastation,
The sun in the clouds, just a glow.

The horizon was frozen,
My destiny had been chosen,
I lay them in a warm nest.

I lay down facing the landscape,
The still image, a constant template,
As I lay down for the eternal rest.

Untitled
Nicole Hammerton
(Inspired by Thomas Hardy's The Difference, The Voice
and The Frozen Greenhouse*)*

How does something so pure turn so poisonous?
Something that is supposed to lift you up
Does nothing but drag you down.
In a moment that thing that people say completed you
Leaves you even more shattered than before.

You hear all of the happiness you should feel
But little do they know all I feel is fear.
You never know what goes on behind closed doors
One smile can hide a world of darkness.

There is such a simple way to end it
If only I had the strength.
Every time I go to leave
The love we once had pulls me back.

Basketball
Ben Horne

Basketball, seen to most as a sport but to many a religion.
The roar of the crowd.
Players fighting to make their family proud.
Driving towards the basket.
Cruising to the playoff bracket.

Fans amazed by colourful shoes and crazy hair.
But when it doesn't go their way suddenly it is not fair.
Referee's bombarded with abuse and petty excuses.

Visiting top colleges watching the talent they produce.
Thinking about the next Lebrons and Currys.
We think about it but really are no worries.

Posters on children's walls.
Right next to a hoop and a child with a ball in his hand.
In his head the clock ticking down.
In an arena filled with sound.
5
4
3
2
1
He might be the player you and your child watch.
Copying their moves.
But for now we'll never know because after all it could be
you or me that go pro.

The Atrocity Exhibition
Joshua Naish

Another PR disaster.
It's coming down, it's over,
Yet again my pride has been the death of me.
But it's just who I am, isn't it?
'*I'm lost in the world.*'[14]

You give me too much power don't you?
You bring me up into such a high and mighty position,
With no real idea of what I'm doing,
I guess it's going to have to be who I am, won't it?
'*I'm lost in the world.*'

This, all of it is your fault,
'*All of the lights,*'[15] just '*run away as fast as you can*'[16]
'*But I have no idea of how I'm gonna function.*'[17]
If one day you just up and leave,
'*I'm lost in the world.*'

Find me a place in this cruel world,
And a reason to stay too,
Now I'm lost, in debt, with an unavoidable void.
'*And I guess that you're at an advantage,
Because you could blame me for everything*'[18]
Begging for the help I need,
'*I'm lost in the world.*'

---

[14] From Kanye West and Justin Vernon's 'Lost in the World'.
[15] From the Lyrics of Kanye West's song of the same title.
[16] From Kanye West's 'Runaway'.
[17] This line may originate with Kanye West. Its origins are, as yet, unknown.
[18] Ibid.

Empty
Kye Smalldon

I love the competition but I feel like it can't get much higher,
I just want it to come down to the wire,
Something that would reignite the fire,
Something to make me tire,
Feeling empty,
Never sweaty,
Have to be dirty,
Call me extraordinary,
Unready,
Then I see them give up already,
Then it happened,
Got named the ace,
Became the captain,
No longer a race,
Became walking pace,
Then came the excuses,
Covered in the bruises,
The game became abusive,
Then there was Judas,
Left the fight,
Wanted to be back in a hurry,
Produced worry,
I beg for more,
Something I can't obtain any more,
For this to be more than a chore
'Sometimes I scare myself'
Trust me I know
It's all just a show
Then it happened
I then laughed again

Frostbite
George Tanton
(Inspired by Thomas Hardy's The Schreckhorn*)*

The wind blew through my fingers,
The church bells rang,
Coldness ran down my legs,
Frostbite was my next thought

The landscape was frozen,
Earth was in motion,
I look around for mountain peaks,
But there were only mountain creeks

'*When Life's dull coils unwind,*'[19]
My greatest thought come to mind,
The sun in the clouds, just a glow,
But there was still an eeriness in the cackle of a crow.

Frostbite in my fingers,
Frostbite in my toes.

---

[19] This line comes from Thomas Hardy's 'The Schreckhorn'.

Paradise
Jessica Whiting

Settling down against her tree,
The sun shining bright,
Her smile was contagious and never-ending,
Her brown eyes glistened,
Climbing among the fluorescent branches,
Butterflies fluttering and birds chirping,
My heart was warm,
But it was her time to go.

My eyes open wide,
The dim grey sky suffocated me,
Her laughter still scatters and her eyes still shine,
She will never see the growth of her life,
Nor the singing of blue birds,
She got carried,
Carried away to paradise.

1830 Hardy's parents' marriage certificate, St Osmund's Church, Melbury Osmund, near Evershot.

The Thomas Hardye School
Dorchester – Dorset

Headteacher: Mike Foley

Apart from ourselves, and our unhappy peculiarities, it is foreign to a man's nature to go on loving a person when he is told that he must and shall be that person's lover. There would be a much likelier chance of his doing it if he were told not to love. If the marriage ceremony consisted in an oath and signed contract between the parties to cease loving from that day forward, in consideration of personal possession being given, and to avoid each other's society as much as possible in public, there would be more loving couples than there are now. Fancy the secret meetings between the perjuring husband and wife, the denials of having seen each other, the clambering in at bedroom windows, and the hiding in closets! There'd be little cooling then.

Extract from *Jude the Obscure* by Thomas Hardy

Eyes open
Ruby Beasley
(Loosely inspired by Wordsworth's A Complaint*)*

There was a change
After vague complaints
And nights of tv dinners

Returning home to quiet tears
After small and silent days
We struggled against mutating fears
That didn't let us sleep

A lot to say, but little said
Something bad began to creep
He did not speak as I expected him to
It's done. It's gone. He's dead.

There was a change
And now it's through.
Eyes open, flowers on the bed.

'A square peg, being forced into a round hole'
James Biley[20]

But how can you blame me?

It would be unfair to call it a gruesome one,
But my life, has made me oh so 'square' ...

Morrisons, Bridport – a selection of differently flavoured tarts.
What was a sweet, sweet flavour
Turned to a bland mush.

He lay there on the cold bathroom tiles, asking for a friend of
his; of which, was not there.
Whilst I, with just my love keeping me going, helped my weak
father drink.
Lapsang Souchong. A tea I still drink to this day.
Holding back the tears (even now), my young self watched
him find the yin, to that moment's yang.

At a neighbour's house, just trying to get away and do what
children do, through a window
I see my aunt moving with haste and sincerity.
She barks how I must get home, straight away.

The house is desolate, silent – not what one expects from a
'standard' household.
A child lost in his own house.
I head up the teal stairs and into my parent's room.

cont ...

---

[20] This poem was published anonymously on pages 115 and 116 in *Inspired by Thomas Hardy: An Anthology of Students' Poems 2019* published by Roving Press for The Thomas Hardy Society. The poem attracted much attention from readers who wanted to know more about the poet. Consequently, it is being republished with the poet's name being made public after obtaining his permission.

There they all are:
Grandma, Mother, Brother and my Aunt.
In the middle:
Father.

Young and innocent, but far from naïve,
I knew what was up.
This was it.
This time, the tears were plentiful.

With myself perched on the bed, we naturally form a circle
around him;
Whether or not he was conscious was not of concern.

'I love you dad. We love you.'

As he passed and his body slumped, a luke warm moisture
engulfed my legs.
His internals finally had the opportunity to relax, once and
for all.
Uncharacteristic of a ten year old, no comments were made
until everyone was ready.
Ready to let go.

Two days later is my birthday, and it must be said:
They have never been the same since.

Now overlooking the countryside, where he lies
In peace.

The Will to Knowledge
Erica Connelly

I lay the senses out on the desk in a row,
One by one by one.
A broadsheet for sight, an encyclopaedia for touch,
A novel for the ears and the Holy Book
for the taste that lingers on your tongue,
In your nose,
In between
These high walls, in here.

Each day the librarian watches
The exchanging of questions and answers
From your hands to hers
Charred memories embedded into the dust of
Fingerprints and fibres of well-turned pages.
Each word holds them, holds you.

'What happened …'
The idea –
'What happened to you is meant to be.'
The idea of a red string –
'By the end of the year, you'll see!'
– Tied around my neck …
The body defies the mind,
Blind rebel. Breathing without command,
Without cause,
Without intention.

I stare at the librarian behind their desk.
Go on, I silently urge, go on.
Our eyes meet –
Nothing.
I'm on my own.

cont …

A man carries a pile of books on Da Vinci, engineering, love,
A child enters the library for his picture book's happy return.
If your own love and hate directs
Your sight and insight,
Perception and misconception,
Then what does it mean that
A girl and her friend study for their exams,
Shoulders hunched over their textbooks
That give the supposed answers
Of how, what, when and why?

The books in front of me are not mine own,
Yet, only I can decipher
Their glossy covers and the blank pages
Littered with machine-pressed
Ink.
The librarian gives us their offering:
God only knows what they mean.

God must be laughing.
A young woman steps afore the shelf ahead of me,
Taunting me with that red ribbon
In her hair.
I could claw it from her scalp.

I scoff.
For each of us, reality is
A story, a metaphor, a simile
Made
In our own eyes.
Sight and insight,
Perception and misconception.
These are all the same.

The librarian, the essential,
Shifts their trolley to the corner, placing
Jude the Obscure in his rightful place.

Experience organises the books
So, in time,
Pain can read.

A magnanimous spirit of gold
Ellie Cornelius

A magnanimous spirit of gold,
She settles on my knee; harping of stardust and a prophecy,
'it's fortuitous,' she proclaimed with a bow of her head,
'it is as tragic as Orpheus and Eurydice'.
With gilded wings she rises – visage turned to the skies,
She tells me to tie my worries to the rays of light,
Cascading from the divine.
Like the strings on a harp she played me well,
As she was not all she seemed.

Roses lie atop her eyes
Paolo Cozzi
(Inspired by Hardy's The Self-Unseeing*)*

Roses lie atop her eyes,
And wilt and whither and decay,
The portly man sings in rhyme,
And feasts above her crumbling grave.

Onlookers echo sympathy,
But don't recall her name,
Denouncing one another with dignity,
But repelled from taking blame.

Her face is plagued with sorrow,
And her legacy forgot,
Whilst we buy and sell and borrow,
And our blood begins to clot.

And our wounds begin to open.
And our breath leaks from our lungs.

Ad Lib
Amélie Nixon

we tend to roll over each other or
dip under, clack like tap shoes,
i move enduringly, patiently.
i'm no dancer but my body is swift,
rhythm is no river but it is confluent,
the dark is dense, hot, leaves no room for shame.
our love is a salvo and not really love:
impatience more fitting. hands like bullets,
hips porous, lighter. the music never stops; neither will we.

'Squirrel' by Amélie Nixon.

The absence of sound deceives the Incessant pounding
Polly Shaw

The absence of sound deceives the incessant pounding,
gaping mouths closed tightly over soft words,
remorsefully swallowing infinite praise and splendour.
The moon and sun tread lightly in those rising hours,
down the path, through the trees,
bodies crashing harmoniously as they run through love's passage.
Their reward, an unspoken certificate of growing pains and
inevitable heartache,
a void of hollow sorrow married to the innocence of youth,
our legs tied to the ground with the dying vines, fed by the
ones we hold with true significance.
Twigs and leaves shall one day encase our fragility, all minds
resolving to black as the sun falls, bitter and broken.

The moon sighs a monotonous cry, jealous and provoked by the
virtuous sun
Who weeps a hapless prayer to the stars.
We sit beneath the wrath, cloaked in ecstasy, fixated on the folds
and curves of our countenance,
parading an ignorance only youth can dismiss.
Shame never ceases to burst through the Clingfilm Curtain.
With improbable resolve we bite tender lips that chip and seep
deep red
blossom, flustered hymen screaming behind closed doors.
Doll like features betray the night time fables of past, pleading the
exhausted moon for time to slow as if in a dream.
Venus comes to meet us with message of her brilliant friend's
arrival,
the glow distantly visible through the sparse branches.
How comfortably I awoke from my slumber, cradled into
consciousness
by my mother's kind song, breaking from your barbed wire
embrace eternally.

The society we call 'modern'
James Sullivan

He is the fog who obtains the brains,
Chops them up and jams them back into us.
Their emotions baffled by society's figure:
Status survived.
Happiness did not. Lost in the
Whirlpool of personalised and meticulously fitted suits
Who own ostentatious Rolls Royces with the motif on looking
down on the drivers of ... Bentleys.

The dove dodges the striking bullets,
As armies of trees, united,
Stand proud,
Hoping they will make a noise, something crudely loud.
The Earth's self-destructive tears,
Turned on by the intoxicating fire burning its lungs and its ears.

Bold opinion is a treat,
A treat we would all like to meet.
Conditioned voices we all want to hear,
Struck down by the oppressed lightning storm.
Happiness would be great in any form.
Yet, all that arrives in our eyes is one subtle tear.

What is 'modern'?
James Sullivan

Modern is sleek architecture, towering above us,
Standing tall. With each skyscraper attempting to greet the
Sky, with a continental kiss perhaps, or just a smile.

Modern is the technology that surrounds us: its perks,
Its dangers. We all know of them – but where is the action?

Modern is people's changing attitudes, demonstrated
through the movements such as: Extinction Rebellion and
Feminism and other anti-discrimination
Groups, scattered protesting here and there (everywhere). A
Single sound or smallest glimpse of one of them is enough
to dispel the outdated tradition who still governs.

Modern is also the widespread fire, stripping life of:
Diversity, identity, personality, peace,
Happiness ... Happiness? What is happiness? Today, it's
Difficult to even define the basic needs of
Any human. Humans who have fought and strived all their lives.

Modern is more than what meets the eye.

Individual Submissions from Other Schools

Grace Bellorine,   The Woodroffe School, Lyme Regis
Emma Boddy,   The Mayfield School, Portsmouth
Esme Houghton-Oliver,   Newton Abbot College, Newton Abbot
Similce Jacobson,   The Woodroffe School, Lyme Regis

Though a good deal is too strange to be believed,
nothing is too strange to have happened.

Extract from *The Personal Notebooks of Thomas Hardy*
by Thomas Hardy

The Acorn Inn, Evershot. Hardy called it 'The Sow and Acorn'
in his Tess of the D'Urbevilles.

Wayfarer
Grace Bellorine

The sadness of Fanny Robin's fate did not make Bathsheba's glorious …
    Burning for burning, wound for wound, strife for strife.

                Extracts from *Far from the Madding Crowd* (Chapter 43)
                                    by Thomas Hardy

I plough
shallow prints into the turnpike track.
Careworn veins of earth
rise to my tread.
I carry
dreams of red:
love-red, hurt-red, hearth-red.
I see
a crow, a smear
of dripping black feathers that I know
will soon enough be skewered:
a black cross on the workhouse door.
A shape
with my shape,
glinting dully in its scarlet eye.
I heave –
And buckle –
And sleep.

cont …

I lie, still,
and you weave sweet petals about my head,
place a pillow of yew to soften your blow,
and brush revenge on my face
with genteel hand.
You rest, weary of anguish,
and take pity with your afternoon tea.

And yet
when I plough quietly upward,
my grave a weeping ruin,
it's you,
mending, as you know how,
kneeling, dress bleeding damp earth into earth.

Other Animals
Emma Boddy
(Inspired by Hardy's The Masked Face*)*

My veins are wrought like wires around a mechanism that doesn't belong to me. I can still hear its scheduled sobs, just as self-pitying as when we were young. It sings its mangled cry with child-like naivety – when I can no longer enslave it with my bloodied breath, it will become plastic. A collectible. Its shiny new value makes me gag. This insatiable fire licks its way up my skin and lungs and teeth and throat, tearing my insides out at the seams and leaving dulled absences in its wake like a decorative afterthought.

I used to put up a fight. An erratic spider trapped under a glass. Now I hang heavy with sedation, alone with my gnawing insides. Why must He fashion me from such tender sentiments only to rip me apart with such detachment? Why must He loom above when He belongs so reluctantly to the animals He's created?

I was never meant to own such a thing as a body. Sickly, sickening violence.

The room is growing colder and my skin is growing thinner; I can feel the machinery pulsing. It's laboured and deliberate. I feel like I can taste the metal melting on my tongue, the kind of taste you can never quite spit out. My room looks the same as it did when I was a child. Light spills under the door and bleeds into the floor like wine. I don't remember closing it.

I trace my brittle fingers along the stain with an instinctive yearning I'm unable to explain. Where do I stop and where does the rest of the world start?

Thump.

cont ...

Thump.

Thump.

It's getting desperate now.

This wasn't how the curtain was supposed to fall, although I know it was never my choice.

My life fleshes out before me in chemical symphonies. My heart thrums in calculated throbs. My loins and nerves and sinew are on fire in orchestrated terror. So much aching and longing and only one life to nurse them; such a sad song and no one to sing it back to me. The light is still washing over my hands with unfamiliar placidity. I wish I could hold onto it. Anything. Anyone.

The cacophony is weeping its last lamenting verse. I hope He can hear it.

Go on.

Finish what you started.

It's just me and you now.

One final chord. One last breath into your bloodbath of Eden.

It was never me who closed the door.

A Response to Thomas Hardy's 'Neutral Tones' from the Female Perspective
Esme Houghton-Oliver

We stood by a pond that winter day
and pensive light shone through soul,
and barren wasteland bowed to trifle leaves annulled,
… stagnant pond rippled further to decay.

Your eyes upon me were as of stone.
Your soliloquy bound hand and foot.
And speaking but a word gritted by soot,
you stripped me to the very bone.

We knew that the day would break,
the rose bud kissed with a frozen touch –
ice in its veins, lifeless within the suffocated clutch,
the bud started to awake …

Since then, sorrows have taught love receives its deeds.
A bloodshed path left crimson red
should lead unhallowed dead,
and a pond edged with sprouting seeds.

Spring step brought around the sunlight verdant,
blushed the glistening beads softened and
rolling down the perennial blossom.
All here is nourished by a sun ardent.

I stood anew by a summer's pond,
new lovers clasped as ivy strong,
relishing the rising phoenix song,
whilst compelled to reminisce the frigid bond.

cont …

My seasons run swift with Demeter's mood,
revelling within love's lush harvest,
and glance down towards our pond once darkest,
frozen lace diverted your face – a shadow abroad.

White of an eye, a moonbeam kiss ...
I walked away from all of this.

Boldwood: Deafening Report
Similce Jacobson

A tear. Loud.
So to raise a sleeping man.
To hold, clasp
A waterskin of her.
Shaking,
Secured in that round,
Cradled tenderly,
Safe,
For one clock
Tick.
Such proud provinces
In your name, I leave.
Used
For sport.

Afterword

Shelley's Skylark
Thomas Hardy
(The neighbourhood of Leghorn: March 1887)

Somewhere afield here something lies
In Earth's oblivious eyeless trust
That moved a poet to prophecies –
A pinch of unseen, unguarded dust

The dust of the lark that Shelley heard,
And made immortal through times to be; –
Though it only lived like another bird,
And knew not its immortality.

Lived its meek life; then, one day, fell –
A little ball of feather and bone;
And how it perished, when piped farewell,
And where it wastes, are alike unknown.

Maybe it rests in the loam I view,
Maybe it throbs in a myrtle's green,
Maybe it sleeps in the coming hue
Of a grape on the slopes of yon inland scene.

Go find it, faeries, go and find
That tiny pinch of priceless dust,
And bring a casket silver-lined,
And framed of gold that gems encrust;

And we will lay it safe therein,
And consecrate it to endless time;
For it inspired a bard to win
Ecstatic heights in thought and rhyme.

I
The Thomas Hardy Creative Workshops 2020 Schemes of Work

The Thomas Hardy Society Council of Management Academic Committee Members: Dr Tracy Hayes, Andrew Hewitt, Dr Karin Koehler, Dr Jonathan Memel, Dr Faysal Mikdadi, Andrew and Marilyn Leah.

> 'It is difficult for a woman to define her feeling in language which is chiefly made by men to express theirs' … Bathsheba was in a very peculiar state of mind, which showed how entirely the soul is the slave of the body, the ethereal spirit dependent for its quality upon the tangible flesh and blood.
>
> Extract from *Far from the Madding Crowd* by Thomas Hardy

The following are suggestions based on proven good practice during the 2018–2019 Thomas Hardy Poetry Workshops and on the students' and their teachers' feedback. Whoever is leading the Creative Workshop should feel free to proceed as s/he sees fit – based on the participants' responses and aptitudes.

- Lead the students in a general discussion on creativity, e.g. composing poems, drawing or painting, performance including acting and dancing, three-dimensional art work, etc. This introductory session should be varied, including, where feasible, participants working in small groups or in pairs and reporting back to the whole group.
- The aims of this session are:
  - ✓ To engage with students within a relaxed and friendly atmosphere.
  - ✓ To elicit from students an acknowledgement of having produced creative works.

✓ To get students to talk about their individual favoured way of being creative.

✓ To encourage students to discuss their own writing (of verse or prose), drawing, painting, performing, designing and making or any activity that they deem to be creative.

✓ To get students to talk about what inspires them to be creative.

✓ Where possible, to get students to talk about a favourite poem, song, picture, creative activity, etc. including ones learnt/seen/ engaged with in childhood.

✓ To imbue students with a sense of worth: their views of the creative urge are sought, appreciated and respected.

✓ To ensure universal participation by engaging all, including seemingly reluctant, students.

✓ To discuss how any creative work takes place.

✓ To show that being creative is both an art form as well as a formulaic process that could be engaged with through inspiration and, often, without.

✓ To share a few Thomas Hardy and other writers' poems/prose as prompts to encourage or inspire a creative response. The possibilities are endless, for example, students attending these Workshops at Max Gate or at Hardy's Cottage are often enthused by anecdotes about Hardy's life, by Emma's experiences in later life, by famous visitors who came to see Hardy, by Hardy's opinions, likes, dislikes, etc.

• The students' booklet contains the following[21]:

Shelley's Skylark	Thomas Hardy
To a Skylark	Percy Bysshe Shelley
The Schreckhorn	Thomas Hardy
'Schreckhorn'	Leslie Stephen
Murmurs in the Gloom	Thomas Hardy
Extract from Ode: Intimations of Immortality from	
Reflections of Early Childhood	William Wordsworth
Zermatt to the Matterhorn	Thomas Hardy
Extract from Hymn	Helen Maria Williams

---

[21] Most of Thomas Hardy's poems and some of his prose extracts used in the Workshops have been included in this Anthology at the start of each section.

Extract from Frankenstein	Mary Shelley
A Bird Song	Christina Rossetti
The Captive Dove	Anne Brontë
To S. M. a Young African Painter on Seeing His Works	Phillis Wheatley
Sympathy	Laurence Dunbar
I Look Into My Glass	Thomas Hardy
An August Midnight	Thomas Hardy
The Darkling Thrush	Thomas Hardy
The Self-Unseeing	Thomas Hardy
A Church Romance	Thomas Hardy
The Difference	Thomas Hardy
The Sun on the Bookcase	Thomas Hardy
The Voice	Thomas Hardy
At the Railway Station, Upway	Thomas Hardy
The Frozen Greenhouse	Thomas Hardy
Extracts from:	
Tess of the D'Urbervilles	Thomas Hardy
The Mayor of Casterbridge	Thomas Hardy
Jude the Obscure	Thomas Hardy

- Engage the students in a conversation on creativity. Should there be any reluctant participant, introduce examples of creative work. Students may talk about their drawings, paintings, designing and making, music compositions and playing, singing, dancing, etc. Try to find as many students' 'inner spark of divine fire' to share, celebrate and to validate individual self-worth.

- Using poetry (or any other art form that you deem suitable for the occasion and the participants) as an example, explain how poems are written, e.g. when the poet is experiencing an overwhelming emotion, after a significant event, on seeing something inspiring, etc. Most importantly, explain that, for now, there is no good poetry (or other creative response) or bad poetry: there is only self-expression within a free and mutually supportive group.

- Ask the students to expand your example of composing poems into other ways of being creative. Encourage them to help you compile a list of creative responses to the one or two or more poems shared. This list helps to focus each individual student's mind on her/his creative outlet. In a few cases, it may help as a creative scaffold to aid students to get started.

- Explain that being creative can be quite artificial and that the creative artist need not suddenly feel inspired or so overwhelmed that s/he has to create. S/he could carefully plan a drawing, carry out the plan, evaluate what s/he has drawn and amend it as needed.

- Ask the students to suggest an occasion worthy of creating an artistic outcome. Choose one or two suggestions and get the group to act on them. For example, on a large surface, the group could collaborate on producing a caricature of – say – a politician or historical figure or, indeed, each other. Suggest that the group could have a go at composing a poem, creating a few dance moves together based on the Hardy poems and other pieces already shared, etc.

- Read a further selection of the pieces included in the Creative Workshop booklet. How many pieces one should read will be determined by the students' responses. Read 'An August Midnight'. Ask for volunteers to help with the readings. Where needed, readers should be given advice on how to read confidently and how to declaim.

- After 'An August Midnight' is read, suggest that when reading a literary piece, there are two things that we are looking for: (1) Immediate meanings or events; and (2) deeper meanings. For example, after reading 'An August Midnight' the following questions on 'immediate meanings' are asked: (a) Where is the poet in this narrative? (In his study.) (b) What is he doing? (Writing.) (c) Who or what comes in? (Four creatures/insects.) (d) What is the fly doing? (Rubbing its hands.) (e) What happens to the poet's page of writing? (The ink is smudged.) The students should be praised for understanding the 'events' of the poem. Now, the following questions on 'deeper meanings' are asked: (a) What do you think the poet is trying to tell us? (A little observation or vignette of something that happened late at night in his study.) (b) Can you support your response with a quotation from the poem? (He describes the light and sounds in the room and then tells us 'On this scene enter …'.) (c) What does the poet think that these four creatures are to start with? ('God's humblest, they!') (d) Why do you think Hardy thinks

121

them so humble? (Probably because of the assumption that these are simple unthinking little creatures motivated only by instinct – not 'thinking' beings like us 'superior' humans.) (e) When he changes his mind, what does he think about these creatures? ('They know Earth-secrets that know not I.') (f) Why does he think that they 'know Earth-secrets that' he does not himself know? (Hardy had a strong respect for all creatures, both human and non-human. Consequently, he was willing to accept that these 'humble' creatures knew things that he, as a human, did not.)

- Give the students a chance to expand on their understanding of the literary piece in any way.

- Ask the students, working alone or in pairs, to re-write lines or short passages in any creative way that they deem fit. Ask them to report back to the whole group by sharing what they have collaboratively written.

- Depending on responses so far, extend the activity or re-writing to include any creative responses that the students wish to have a go at. Responses could include written work (poem, narrative, description, etc.) or artwork of their choice (drawing, painting, performance piece such as dance, drama, recitation, etc.).

- The process is repeated with other pieces. As each response is read, performed, displayed, etc. outcomes could be discussed, analysed and 'amended/improved'. Students are encouraged to take risks if they wished. Seek variety from the students and encourage different approaches, ideas, expressions, forms, structures and styles.

- If interludes are needed, stop the process and introduce one of the following light-hearted 'games': (1) Exquisite Corpses: Write a first line of a poem. Pass the paper to a student who writes a second line. Before s/he passes the paper on to the next student, s/he bends the paper so that the first line cannot be seen and the next writer sees only the previous line just written. The third writer writes a line continuing the second line and bends the paper so that his/her line is the only one that can be seen by the fourth writer, etc. At the end of the process the paper returns to the one who had written the first line. Read the finished poem out. Ask one or more students to re-read the poem to everyone. Encourage a discussion on whether the poem makes sense, is cohesive, etc. As a group, the poem may be edited to 'improve' it. (2) Collaborative Genius: A first line is written and the paper is passed on without hiding any previous writing. As the paper goes around the room, each student adds one line, etc. The paper comes back to the first writer who then reads it out. A discussion similar to that for (1) above takes place. (3) Guessing Games: Volunteer(s) would, say, perform a brief dance or mime. Those watching try to link what they see to one of the creative passage(s) previously shared. (4) Mime: A confident adult present could be asked to mime a specific event/impression/pronouncement elicited from one of the creative passages shared from the booklet. Those watching would then guess where it comes from or what it means.

- During breaks, seek out reluctant participants and engage them in discussions on any subject that emerges naturally. Encourage them to talk freely and praise their responses. Suggest that you and others would really be interested in hearing their views on creativity and ask them to consider participating in any way that they feel comfortable doing when the group gets back together after the break.

- Ask the following questions before moving on to the next piece(s): (1) Do poems have to make sense? (2) Do poems have to rhyme? (3) What matters more; the meaning or the sound? (4) How long or short should a poem be? What possible poetic devices can the students think of – with examples where possible? (5) Can a narrative be turned into a poem (e.g. Henchard selling his wife)?

- The students can have between thirty minutes and one hour to create their own responses to any of the creative passages shared. On some rare occasions, two close friends may collaborate on doing so. Students may produce whatever they wish. If they need a framework or writing scaffold, they may use any passage from the little booklet, emulate it or, if they feel the need, borrow from it (ask the students doing so to ensure that what they borrow is clearly placed within inverted commas to acknowledge that the words are not theirs). The outcome of this independent work may include written pieces, artwork, performance piece, etc. If a student produces little or nothing, ensure that s/he is not in any way 'shown up'. The following, albeit negative, are perfectly acceptable student responses: 'I don't do poetry'; 'I hate art'; 'I've never liked drama' … As adults, our only response to these statements should be a smile and a gentle question, 'What do you enjoy doing?' Every student has an inner creative/artistic urge desperate to realise itself and to be recognised by those in her/his life.

- Once the creative session is over, each student is encouraged to present what they have created. After each presentation, students are asked to give only positive comments to start with. Whatever comment they make, they should be challenged to offer evidence from the presentation. After all the positive comments are made, students are asked to be critical friends and to suggest what could be done better (with clear reference to the presentation being critically appreciated).

- After the whole session is over, the students' creative works are displayed in public areas around the school or published in/ on school publications/media. Students able or willing to do so should be encouraged to share their works at school-based events both with their peers, their family and the local community. Their creative works should be entered into as many competitions as may be available for their various age ranges.

- Where possible, cost and space permitting, The Thomas Hardy Society will undertake to publish or display or publicise the students' creative works. It is important to brief the students on such a possibility by ensuring that they all understand that there is no guarantee of any publication because of the sheer scale of the number of students taking part and because of the potential cost. What the students can be promised is that The Thomas Hardy Society would do all that may be possible to disseminate their works to the widest audience possible depending on cost and available opportunities.

- There are extracts from three Thomas Hardy novels included in the students' booklet. Workshop Leaders may wish to give a very brief narrative context before sharing any of the three extracts. Strictly speaking, this may not be necessary. However, giving such a quick synopsis may prompt some students to read one or more novels.

II

Sample 'Guidelines to Workshop Facilitators'

Ah, there's too much of that sending to school in these days. It only does harm. Every gate-post and barn's door you come to is sure to have some bad word or other chalked upon it by the young rascals: a woman can hardly pass for shame sometimes. If they'd never been taught how to write they wouldn't have been able to scribble such villany. Their fathers couldn't do it, and the country was all the better for it.

Extract from *The Return of the Native* by Thomas Hardy

The *Schemes of Work* booklet has been compiled for use mainly by schools that have agreed to run their own programme of the Thomas Hardy Creative Workshops 2020.

It is also intended as a guide to Thomas Hardy Creative Workshops 2020 Leaders who have kindly volunteered to share their love of literature with students.

These Workshop Plans are only suggestions. Workshop Leaders should feel free to run each Creative Workshop as they see fit. The listed poems and prose passages may be used, although, if Workshop Leaders wish to use other pieces, that is entirely up to each individual.

Whereas the main focus is acquainting participants with Thomas Hardy's writings, other writers have been included because of the Thomas Hardy Poetry Workshops 2019 students' requests. Where possible, writings selected can be fairly easily linked to Hardy's own works. This would allow some students to be further challenged by comparing and contrasting other writers with Hardy.

There are only three tasks that each Thomas Hardy Creative Workshop Leader needs to complete. The reason for this request is to ensure some inner cohesion, to fulfil safeguarding requirements and to keep to deadlines imposed by various external imperatives. Submissions can be made at any time before, or at one go by, 6 April 2020.

These three 'mandatory' tasks are as follows:

(1) Parental Permission Forms must be completed by the adult(s) responsible, collected by the Workshop Leader directly or through the school. All completed Forms must be submitted to the Academic Director. Schools and participants should be alerted that if parental permission is not given, their work cannot be taken forward to public dissemination.

(2) Student Evaluation Forms must be completed either by each individual participant or, more manageably, by the Workshop Leader after a group discussion at the end of the session. The Workshop Leader could then submit a brief list of the main items raised in the evaluation discussion.

(3) All students' work must be submitted to the Academic Director by 6 April 2020. Written work may be e-mailed directly to fhm481812@aol.com. Other works, e.g. paintings, drawings, performances, etc. may be submitted as good-quality photographs, CD recordings/videos and other related media readily available.

III

Errata in Inspired by Thomas Hardy: An Anthology of Students' Poems 2019

Well, well! All's past amend,
Unchangeable. It must go.
I seem but a dead man held on end
To sink down soon ...

Extract from 'The Going' by Thomas Hardy

The published edition of *Inspired by Thomas Hardy: An Anthology of Students' Poems 2019* contained the two errors detailed below.

The National Trust Visitor Experience Manager was erroneously referred to as 'Martin Steven' on page xi. The proper spelling of the surname is Stephen.

The second error on the same page was with reference to Michelle Caesar's professional designation at the National Trust. This is given as (Visiting Experience Officer) when it should be (Visitor Experience Officer).

I wish to apologise for both errors for which I take full responsibility as the Editor of the Anthology. No discourtesy whatsoever was intended to either Martin Stephen or Michelle Caesar. Both Martin and Michelle were very courteous in forgiving my error.

IV

List of Participants

... every word in both Latin and Greek was to be individually committed to memory at the cost of years of plodding. Jude flung down the books, lay backward along the broad trunk of the elm, and was an utterly miserable boy for the space of a quarter of an hour ... What brains they must have in Christminster and the great schools, he presently thought, to learn words one by one up to tens of thousands! There were no brains in his head equal to this business; and as the little sun-rays continue to stream in through his hat at him, he wished he had never seen a book, that he might never see another, that he had never been born.

Extract from *Jude the Obscure* by Thomas Hardy

List of Participating Schools:

1. Bryanston School
2. Cape Cornwall School – postponed due to the national school closure in March 2020
3. Dorchester Middle School
4. Dorset Studio School
5. Greenwood Academy
6. St Ives School – postponed due to the national school closure in March 2020
7. St Osmund's Church of England Middle School
8. Southlands School
9. The Taunton Academy
10. The Thomas Hardye School
11. Trewirgie Junior School – postponed due to the national school closure in March 2020

Schools from which students contributed a poem:

The Mayfield School
Newton Abbot College
The Woodroffe School

V

Outcomes Expected

The whole secret of fiction and the drama – in the constructional part – lies in the adjustment of things unusual to things eternal and universal. The writer who knows exactly how exceptional, and how non-exceptional, his events should be made, possesses the key to the art.

Extract from *The Life of Thomas Hardy* by Thomas Hardy
(with additions by Florence Hardy; edited by Michael Millgate)

Please ensure that all work submitted by students is sent to Faysal Mikdadi by 6 April 2020 (fhm481812@aol.com).

Where possible, submissions would be preferred as e-mail attachments so that editing is made easier by copying and pasting.

Any students' creative responses other than written pieces, e.g. drawings, paintings, performing arts, 3-D creations, etc. should be photographed or, where appropriate, filmed and submitted using the e-mail fhm481812@aol.com.

Photographs should be of good quality in order to allow for reproductions in print. They should have the following resolutions:
300 dpi for colour pictures;
300 to 600 dpi for black and white pictures;
600 to 900 dpi for combination art (i.e. photograph and text); and
900 to 1200 dpi for line art.

Whereas late submissions are not acceptable, there are occasions when they occur for reasons beyond the individual student's control. If, for any reason deemed acceptable to the Workshop Leader, submissions need to be made after the date set above (6 April 2020), please alert Faysal Mikdadi in order to ensure that editing takes into account late submissions by creating a space for their late arrival.

Please ensure that permission to use any photograph is always obtained from the person who took it. These include photographs downloaded on-line even if they are out of copyright. For example, a photograph of Thomas Hardy may be out of copyright in itself, but permission for its use must come from the Website Administrator. Furthermore, where a photograph of, for example, a framed image of Emma Hardy is taken at Max Gate, the National Trust's permission must be sought both for taking as well as for using the photograph. There may be a cost/fee attached. Any such permission obtained must accompany any photograph submitted so that an acknowledgement is always made.

VI

Parent/Guardian Permissions Form

The Thomas Hardy Society is running one or more Thomas Hardy Creative Workshops at your child's school.

Please complete this form and return to the school. Thank you.

Name of your child: ....

Please delete as appropriate below:

1. I give permission for my child to attend the Workshop(s)
   Yes / No   (delete as applicable)

2. I give permission for my child's work to be published or displayed:
   Yes / No   (delete as applicable)

3. If 'Yes' to 2. above, I wish my child's work to be acknowledged by:
   Full Name / Anonymously   (delete as applicable)

4. In the event of my child's work being displayed, published or publicised through a media outlet, I give permission for the following:
   Name only   (delete as applicable)
   Photograph only   (delete as applicable)
   Photograph & name   (delete as applicable)
   None of the above   (delete as applicable)

If you have any queries about the Workshop(s) please e-mail Faysal Mikdadi – Academic Director of The Thomas Hardy Society, on fhm481812@aol.com.

VII

Student Evaluation Form

As to reviewing. Apart from a few brilliant exceptions, poetry is not at bottom criticized as such, that is, as a particular man's artistic interpretation of life, but with a secret eye on its theological and political propriety. Swinburne used to say to me so it would be two thousand years hence; but I doubt it ... [Swinburne and I] laughed & condoled with each other on having been the two most abused of living writers – he for *'Poems & Ballads'* & I for *'Jude the Obscure'*.

Extract from *The Life of Thomas Hardy* by Thomas Hardy
(with additions by Florence Hardy; edited by Michael Millgate)

Note to Workshop Leader: Evaluation Forms must be completed either by each individual participant or, more manageably, by the Workshop Leader after a group discussion at the end of the session. The Workshop Leader could then submit a brief list of the main items raised in the evaluation discussion along with submissions made on or by 6 April 2020.

...

Thank you for taking part in today's Workshop. In order to keep improving these sessions in the future, your views would be very helpful.

Please list the things that you felt went well during today's Workshop:

✓ ....

✓ ....

✓ ....

✓ ....

Please list the things that could be done better in the future:

Χ ....

Χ ....

Χ ....

Χ ....

VIII

Southlands School
Lymington – Hampshire

Southlands School is an Ofsted-Registered independent specialist school, offering 38-week through to 52-week residential and day placements for boys and girls aged 7–19 years old with a diagnosis of Asperger's Syndrome on the Autistic Spectrum.[22]

The Thomas Hardy School Creative Workshops 2020
Students' Booklet

Contents

A Bird Song	Christina Rossetti
The Captive Dove	Anne Brontë
An August Midnight	Thomas Hardy
The Self-Unseeing	Thomas Hardy
A Church Romance	Thomas Hardy
At the Railway Station, Upway	Thomas Hardy
The Frozen Greenhouse	Thomas Hardy
Maumbury Ring (Mary Channing's Execution)	Thomas Hardy

Strangled and burnt at the stake [23]
Thomas Channing's Will [24]
Photograph of Thomas Hardy in Old Age [25]
Photograph of Thomas Hardy in His Study [26]

---

[22] Extract from the School's website: https://www.cambiangroup.com/specialist-education/our-schools/asperger-schools/southlands-school/.
Note: The four pictures used in the Southlands Students' Booklet have not been reproduced in this book. Each image may be viewed on the internet through the links given below.
[23] https://sites.rootsweb.com/~fordingtondorset/Files2/ExecutionMaryChanning1704.html.
[24] Thomas Channing's Will – leaving all to his father apart from one Shilling (five pence in today's money) to his wife Mary – can be found at https://sites.rootsweb.com/~fordingtondorset/Files2/ExecutionMaryChanning1704.html.
[25] https://www.britannica.com/biography/Thomas-Hardy/Legacy.
[26] https://www.irishtimes.com/opinion/the-hardy-way-an-irishman-s-diary-on-thomas-hardy-in-ireland-1.3266015.

A Bird Song
Christina Rossetti

It's a year almost that I have not seen her:
Oh, last summer green things were greener,
Brambles fewer, the blue sky bluer.

It's surely summer, for there's a swallow:
Come one swallow, his mate will follow,
The bird race quicken and wheel and thicken.

Oh happy swallow whose mate will follow
O'er height, o'er hollow! I'd be a swallow,
To build this weather one nest together.

<u>Notes:</u>
The poet is comparing the way that swallows live and work together – mating
and breeding for life. Being alone is hard, especially now that it has been *'a year
almost that [the speaker has] not seen her'*. The swallows mating for life makes
the speaker think of the ideal relationship.

The Captive Dove
Anne Brontë

Poor restless dove, I pity thee;
And when I hear thy plaintive moan,
I mourn for thy captivity,
And in thy woes forget mine own.
To see thee stand prepared to fly,
And flap those useless wings of thine,
And gaze into the distant sky,
Would melt a harder heart than mine.

In vain – in vain! Thou canst not rise:
Thy prison roof confines thee there;
Its slender wires delude thine eyes,
And quench thy longings with despair.

Oh, thou wert made to wander free
In sunny mead and shady grove,
And, far beyond the rolling sea,
In distant climes, at will to rove!

Yet, hadst thou but one gentle mate
Thy little drooping heart to cheer,
And share with thee thy captive state,
Thou couldst be happy even there.

Yes, even there, if, listening by,
One faithful dear companion stood,
While gazing on her full bright eye,
Thou mightst forget thy native wood.

But thou, poor solitary dove,
Must make, unheard, thy joyless moan;
The heart, that Nature formed to love,
Must pine, neglected, and alone.

An August Midnight
Thomas Hardy

I
A shaded lamp and a waving blind,
And the beat of a clock from a distant floor:
On this scene enter – winged, horned, and spined –
A longlegs, a moth, and a dumbledore;   *dumbeldore: bumblebee*
While 'mid my page there idly stands
A sleepy fly, that rubs its hands ...

II
Thus meet we five, in this still place,
At this point of time, at this point in space.
– My guests besmear my new-penned line,   *besmear: smear over/stain*
Or bang at the lamp and fall supine.   *supine: lazily inactive/listless*
'God's humblest, they!' I muse. Yet why?
They know Earth-secrets that know not I

Max Gate, 1899

Notes[27]:
'Hardy's reverence for all life had some basis in his reading in science, in evolutionary theory, all living things are akin ...' Hardy once remarked: "'I often wonder how much animals know – about things – things of which we are 'ignorant'." The 'Earth secrets' that he supposed the insects might know are not earth's meanings. They do not know more than the poet does, but each perceives something the other does not.'

[27] Notes on poems by Thomas Hardy are based on *The Poetry of Thomas Hardy – A Handbook and Commentary* by J. O. Bailey, The University of North Carolina Press, Chapel Hill, USA, 1970.

The Self-Unseeing
Thomas Hardy

Here is the ancient floor,
Footworn and hollowed and thin,
Here was the former door
Where the dead feet walked in.

She sat here in her chair,
Smiling into the fire;
He who played stood there,
Bowing it higher and higher.

Childlike, I danced in a dream;
Blessings emblazoned that day;   *emblazoned: displayed brightly*
Everything glowed with a gleam;
Yet we were looking away!

Notes:
This poem *'presents Hardy's nostalgic meditation during a visit to his boyhood home at Higher Bockhampton ... The characters are himself, his father, and his mother.'* Hardy as a child was no more than four years old dancing to his father's playing of the violin.

137

A Church Romance
(Mellstock *circa* 1835)
Thomas Hardy

She turned in the high pew, until her sight
Swept the west gallery, and caught its row
Of music-men with viol, book, and bow
Against the sinking sad tower-window light.

She turned again; and in her pride's despite
One strenuous viol's inspirer seemed to throw
A message from his string to her below,
Which said: 'I claim thee as my own forthright!'

Thus their hearts' bond began, in due time signed.
And long years thence, when Age had scared Romance,
At some old attitude of his or glance
That gallery-scene would break upon her mind,
With him as minstrel, ardent, young, and trim,   minstrel: singer or musician
Bowing 'New Sabbath' or 'Mount Ephraim'.

Notes:
This poem tells the story of Thomas Hardy's parents' first meeting in their local
church. The poet's grandfather *'led the choir at Stinsford Church, playing the
'cello. The other instrumentalists were his sons, Thomas and James ... This
choir performed twice each Sunday in the now-demolished West Gallery of the
Church.'*

At the Railway Station, Upway
Thomas Hardy

'There is not much that I can do,
    For I've no money that's quite my own!'
    Spoke up the pitying child –
A little boy with a violin
At the station before the train came in, –
'But I can play my fiddle to you,
And a nice one 'tis, and good in tone!'

  The man in the handcuffs smiled;
The constable looked, and he smiled, too,
  As the fiddle began to twang;
And the man in the handcuffs suddenly sang
      With grimful glee: *grimful: frightful/not yielding*
      'This life so free
      Is the thing for me!'
And the constable smiled, and said no word,
As if unconscious of what he heard;
And so they went on till the train came in –
The convict, and boy with the violin.

Notes:
"'Upway' for Upwey, a village on the River Wey about three and half miles south of Dorchester ... The prisoner is probably being taken to Portland Prison on the Isle of Portland.'

The Frozen Greenhouse
Thomas Hardy
(St Juliot)

'There was a frost
Last night!' she said,
'And the stove was forgot
When we went to bed,
And the greenhouse plants
Are frozen dead!'

By the breakfast blaze
Blank-faced spoke she,
Her scared young look
Seeming to be
The very symbol
Of tragedy.

The frost is fiercer
Than then to-day,
As I pass the place
Of her once dismay,
But the greenhouse stands
Warm, tight, and gay,

While she who grieved
At the sad lot
Of her pretty plants –
Cold, iced, forgot –
Herself is colder,
And knows it not.

Notes:
'"The Frozen Greenhouse", Hardy's biographers have assumed, is autobiographical. In describing Emma Gifford, who became the first Mrs. Hardy, Evelyn Hardy says: "She loved animals and growing things and once, when the greenhouse stove at the Rectory had been neglected and all the plants had died, her face became 'the very symbol of tragedy'." Weber dates the event as the day of Hardy's departure after his first visit to St. Juliot, Friday, March 11, 1870. He says that on the morning of Hardy's departure, Emma "struck a light six times in her anxiety to call the servants early enough to get the architect off on time for his return journey". Hardy's poem "The Frozen Greenhouse" tells us something about that morning. The greenhouse is still standing.'

Maumbury Ring (and the Execution of Mary Channing)
Thomas Hardy

The Amphitheatre was a huge circular enclosure, with a notch at opposite extremities of its diameter north and south. From its sloping internal form it might have been called the spittoon of Jötuns ... Melancholy, impressive, lonely, yet accessible from every part of the town, the historic circle was the frequent spot for appointments of a furtive kind. Intrigues were arranged there; tentative meetings were there experimented after divisions and feuds ... its associations had about them something sinister ... Apart from the sanguinary nature of the games originally played therein, such incidents attached to its past as these: that for scores of years the town-gallows had stood at one corner; that in 1705 a woman who had murdered her husband was half-strangled and then burnt there in the presence of ten thousand spectators. Tradition reports that at a certain stage of the burning her heart burst and leapt out of her body, to the terror of them all, and that not one of those ten thousand people ever cared particularly for hot roast after that.

Extract from *The Mayor of Casterbridge* by Thomas Hardy

(The following is an extract from *Thomas Hardy's Personal Writings.*)[28]

The present month sees the last shovelful filled in, the last sod replaced, of the excavations in the well-known amphitheatre at Dorchester, which have been undertaken at the instance of the Dorset Field and Antiquarian Club and others, for the purpose of ascertaining the history and date of the ruins. The experts have scraped their spades and gone home to meditate on the results of their exploration, pending the resumption of the work next spring. Mr. St. George Gray, of Taunton, has superintended the labour, assisted by Mr. Charles Prideaux, an enthusiastic antiquary of the town, who, with disinterested devotion to discovery, has preferred to spend his annual holiday from his professional duties at the bottom of chalk trenches groping for fibulae or arrow-heads in a drizzling rain, to idling it away on any other spot in Europe.[29]

---

[28] Thomas Hardy's entire piece was presented to the students at Southlands. The extracts reproduced here are the ones that were focused on during the readings. The full original passage may be accessed at https://www.executedtoday. com/2017/03/21/1706-mary-channing-at-the-maumbury-rings/.
[29] The Students' Booklet includes a photograph of the [Maumbury] amphitheatre today, taken by © Carron Brown, which may be accessed at https://www.flickr. com/photos/carron/7409187794/.

As usual, revelations have been made of an unexpected kind. There was a moment when the blood of us onlookers ran cold, and we shivered a shiver that was not occasioned by our wet feet and dripping clothes. For centuries the town, the county, and England generally, novelists, poets, historians, guidebook writers, and what not, had been freely indulging their imaginations in picturing scenes that, they assumed, must have been enacted within those oval slopes; the feats, the contests, animal exhibitions, even gladiatorial combats, before throngs of people

> Who loved the games men played with death,
> Where death must win.

– briefly, the Colosseum programme on a smaller scale. But up were thrown from one corner prehistoric implements, chipped flints, horns, and other remains, and a voice announced that the earthworks were of the Palaeolithic or Neolithic age, and not Roman at all!

This, however, was but a temporary and, it is believed, unnecessary alarm ...

... Maumbury was the scene of as sinister an event as any associated with it, because it was a definite event. It is one which darkens its concave to this day. This was the death suffered there on March 21, 1705–6, of a girl who had not yet reached her nineteenth year. Here, at any rate, we touch real flesh and blood, and no longer uncertain visions of possible Romans at their games or barbarians at their sacrifices. The story is a ghastly one, but nevertheless very distinctly a chapter of Maumbury's experiences. This girl was the wife of a grocer in the town, a handsome young woman 'of good natural parts', and educated 'to a proficiency suitable enough to one of her sex, to which likewise was added dancing'. She was tried and condemned for poisoning her husband, a Mr. Thomas Channing, to whom she had been married against her wish by the compulsion of her parents. The present writer has examined more than once a report of her trial, and can find no distinct evidence that the thoughtless, pleasure-loving creature committed the crime, while it contains much to suggest that she did not. Nor is any motive discoverable for such an act. She was allowed to have her former lover or lovers about her by her indulgent and weak-minded husband, who permitted her to go her own ways, give parties, and supplied her with plenty of money. However, at the assizes at the end of July, she was found guilty, after a trial in which the testimony chiefly went to show her careless character before and after marriage.

142

During the three sultry days of its continuance, she, who was soon to become a mother, stood at the bar – then, as may be known, an actual bar of iron – 'by reason of which (runs the account) and her much talking, being quite spent, she moved the Court for the liberty of a glass of water'. She conducted her own defence with the greatest ability, and was complimented thereupon by Judge Price, who tried her, but did not extend his compliment to a merciful summing-up. Maybe that he, like Pontius Pilate, was influenced by the desire of the townsfolk to wreak vengeance on somebody, right or wrong. When sentence was about to be passed, she pleaded her condition; and execution was postponed. Whilst awaiting the birth of her child in the old damp gaol by the river at the bottom of the town, near the White Hart inn, which stands there still, she was placed in the common room for women prisoners and no bed provided for her, no special payment and no bed provided for her, no special payment having been made to her goaler, Mr. Knapton, for a separate cell. Someone obtained for her the old tilt of a wagon to screen her from surrounding eyes, and under this she was delivered of a son, in December. After her lying-in she was attacked with an intermittent fever of a violent and lasting kind, which preyed upon her until she was nearly wasted away. In this state, at the next assizes, on the 8th of March following, the unhappy woman, who now said that she longed for death, but still persisted in her innocence, was again brought to the bar, and her execution fixed for the 21st.

On that day two men were hanged before her turn came, and then, 'the under-sheriff having taken some refreshment', he proceeded to his biggest and last job with this girl not yet 19, now reduced to a skeleton by the long fever, and already more dead than alive. She was conveyed from the gaol in a cart 'by her father's and husband's houses', so that the course of the procession must have been up the High-East-street as far as the Bow, thence down South-street and up the straight old Roman road to the Ring beside it. 'When fixed to the stake she justified her innocence to the very last, and left the world with a courage seldom found in her sex. She being first strangled, the fire was kindled about five in the afternoon, and in the sight of many thousands she was consumed to ashes.' There is nothing to show that she was dead before the burning began, and from the use of the word 'strangled' and not 'hanged', it would seem that she was merely rendered insensible before the fire was lit. An ancestor of the present writer, who witnessed the scene, has handed down the information that 'her heart leapt out' during the burning, and other curious details that cannot be printed here. Was man ever 'slaughtered by his fellow man' during the Roman or barbarian use of this place of games or of sacrifice in circumstances of greater atrocity?

A melodramatic, though less gruesome, exhibition within the arena was that which occurred at the time of the 'No Popery' riots, and was witnessed by this writer when a small child. Highly realistic effigies of the Pope and Cardinal Wiseman were borne in procession from Fordington Hill round the town, followed by a long train of mock priests, monks, and nuns, and preceded by a young man discharging Roman candles, till the same wicked old place was reached, in the centre of which there stood a huge rick of furze, with a gallows above. The figures were slung up, and the fire blazed till they were blown to pieces by fireworks contained within them ...